The Whole Story

Richard Rossner

ACKNOWLEDGEMENTS

We are grateful to the following copyright holders for permission to reproduce short stories:

Authors' agents for 'Dead Man's Path' by C. Achebe from *Girls at War* pub. Heinemann Educational Books Ltd; authors' agents for 'Embroidery' by Ray Bradbury from *Marvel Science Fiction* pub. Stadium Publishing (c) 1951 by Stadium Publishing Co. renewed 1979 by Ray Bradbury; Jonathan Cape Ltd on behalf of the Executors of the Ernest Hemingway Estate & Charles Scribner's Sons for 'Old Man at the Bridge' from *The Short Stories of Ernest Hemingway* (c) 1939 Ernest Hemingway, copyright renewed (c) 1966 Mary Hemingway; Andre Deutsch Ltd for 'Heat' by Jean Rhys from *Sleep it off Lady*; authors' agents for 'You Are Now Entering the Human Heart' by Janet Frame pub. The Women's Press (c) Janet Frame 1983; authors' agents for 'I Spy' by Graham Greene from *Collected Stories* pub. Wm Heinemann Ltd & The Bodley Head; Hamish Hamilton Ltd for 'Eye Witness' by Ed McBain from *McBain Brief* (c) 1982 Hui Corporation; A. Norah Hartley for 'A High Dive' by L. P. Hartley pub. Hamish Hamilton; William Heinemann Ltd for 'A Shadow' from *Malgudi Days* by R. K. Narayan; Longman Group UK Ltd for 'A Tree Falls' from *Listen, the Wind and Other Stories* by Roger Mais ed. K. Ramchand in *Longman Caribbean Writers Series*; authors' agents for 'Tell us about the Turkey Jo' by Alan Marshall, (c) Jenny O'Mara & Cathy Marshall; authors' agents & The William Saroyan Literary Foundation for 'The First Day at School' by William Saroyan from *Best Stories of William Saroyan*.

We are grateful to the following copyright holders for permission to record short stories:

Authors' agents for 'Dead Man's Path' by C. Achebe from *Girls at War* pub. Heinemann Educational Books Ltd; authors' agents for 'Embroidery' by Ray Bradbury from *Marvel Science Fiction* pub. Stadium Publishing (c) 1951 by Stadium Publishing Co. renewed 1979 by Ray Bradbury; Andre Deutsch Ltd for 'Heat' by Jean Rhys from *Sleep it off Lady*; authors' agents for 'You Are Now Entering the Human Heart' by Janet Frame pub. The Woman's Press (c) Janet Frame 1983; authors' agents for 'I Spy' by Graham Greene from *Collected Stories* pub. Wm Heinemann Ltd & The Bodley Head; A. Norah Hartley for 'A High Dive' by L. P. Hartley pub. Hamish Hamilton; Longman Group UK Ltd for 'A Tree Falls' from *Listen, the Wind and Other Stories* by Roger Mais ed. K. Ramchand in *Longman Caribbean Writers Series*; authors' agents for 'Tell us about the Turkey Jo' by Alan Marshall (c) Jenny O'Mara & Cathy Marshall; authors' agents for 'Eye Witness' by Ed McBain from *McBain Brief* pub. Hamish Hamilton (c) 1982 Hui Corporation; authors' agents for 'A Shadow' by R. K. Narayan from *Malgudi Days* pub. Wm Heinemann Ltd; authors' agents & The William Saroyan Literary Foundation for 'The First Day at School' by William Saroyan from *Best Stories of William Saroyan*.

We regret that permission was not granted for the recording of 'Old Man at the Bridge' by Ernest Hemingway.

I would like to thank in particular Kate Goldrick and the advisors for their helpful comments on drafts of this manuscript, and Sue Parker and other staff at the Bell Language Institute for piloting an earlier version.

We are grateful to the following for permission to reproduce copyright photographs:

J. Allan Cash Limited for pages 12 (left), 20 (left) and 27 (right); Banana UK Photo Library for pages 27 (left) and 75 (right); Camera Press Limited for pages 35 (left), 41, 49, 73, 82 (right), 94 and 102; James Davis Photography for page 96 (left); The Telegraph Colour Library Limited for page 51 (left); Art Directors Photo Library for page 51 (right); Susan Griggs Agency Limited for page 82 (left); Guinness Book of Records for page 67 (left); The Hutchison Library for page 12 (right), 20 (right) and 35 (right); Longman Cheshire Pty Limited for page 26; Longman Group UK Limited for pages 33, 56 and 65; Network Photographers for page 58 (right); The Photo Source Limited for pages 89 (right) and 96 (right); Picturepoint Limited for pages 58 (left) and 75 (left); Popperfoto for pages 18, 43 (left) and 67 (right); Topham Picture Library for page 43 (right); Viewfinder Colour Photo Library for page 89 (left); The Women's Press for page 87.

Longman Group UK Limited,
Longman House, Burnt Mill, Harlow,
Essex CM20 2JE, England
and Associated Companies throughout the world.

© Longman Group UK Limited 1988

First published 1988
Seventh impression 1992

Set in Linotron Times
Produced by Longman Singapore Publishers (Pte) Ltd.
Printed in Singapore

ISBN 0-582-79109-X

CONTENTS

TO THE TEACHER

The art of story-telling is well-developed in all cultures, and the short story has long been a favourite among readers. This makes the short story an ideal resource in language teaching and learning. In the English language, learners are fortunate to have at their disposal a very wide range of stimulating and accessible stories. This is so because it is not just British and American authors who have favoured the short story: African, Indian, Caribbean and Australasian writers have also contributed to the rich pool of stories in English.

This collection brings together a dozen stories from around the world which are short enough in their original form to be read as part of an English language course by upper-intermediate and advanced learners of English (including those preparing for examinations like the Cambridge First Certificate and beyond). The aims are to encourage learners to believe that they can enjoy reading creative writing in English, by providing them with activities that may help them 'get into' the stories quickly and easily and explore the meaning fully. The exercises aim to use the stories as a springboard for the consolidation and development of vocabulary and reading skills; however, many teachers will also see ways of working on grammar or discourse, according to their particular learners' needs. In addition, the exercises aim to use the stories as a stimulating starting point for discussion and writing. In the activities before and after the story, students are encouraged to relate their own experiences and opinions to those projected in the stories as they move towards a full understanding of the language used. In other words, the stories are seen both as rich comprehensible input and a stimulus for real communication in English. Moreover, the stories, and the exercises that focus on ways in which writers achieve the effects they do, may be useful in the introductory phase of a literature-orientated course. But the most important aim is to get students reading real stories in their original form for pleasure. After using this book learners will be prepared to look forward to reading 'literature' with enjoyment.

Using the book in class

The Whole Story is an anthology, so there is no need for learners to do the stories in the order presented. The only principle in sequencing is a childhood to old age development. The stories are similar in length, but some contain more unfamiliar vocabulary than others, so it is wise to select them carefully. The texts are roughly graded as follows (A is easier, C more difficult); please note that this is a subjective guide.

Level A 1, 3, 4, 11   *Level B* 2, 6, 9, 10   *Level C* 5, 7, 8, 12

You will find that there are many potential thematic links and contrasts among the stories, and these can be built on whatever the order preferred.

Pre-reading activities

These normally comprise:

a) An activity to introduce the topic, or one of the topics, of the story. The aim is to get learners to approach the story with a degree of personal 'readiness', so that whatever difficulties they may have actually reading it will not be exacerbated by coming to it with no mental or linguistic preparation. Normally the activity asks them to look at the topic in question from the perspective of personal experience or reflection. In this way certain common ground is established between the learner-reader and the writer or protagonist.

b) the themes of the stories usually mean that clear vocabulary areas are explored. Where I have felt learners might benefit from pre-reading work with some of the vocabulary involved, I have included a 'word-exploration' activity. Often, however, sufficient vocabulary arises in the pre-reading activity.

c) I have deliberately not provided for much overt 'prediction' work, partly because there are methodological doubts about it: when does one ever overtly predict the content and meaning of what one is reading or listening to? It happens implicitly. However, the discussion related to the two pictures in each unit is a means of orientation to the story. In addition, some teachers may wish to have students tell each other their own stories or anecdotes by way of warming up, or to use the story titles as a stimulus for pre-reading discussion. Others may want to intersperse learners' actual reading of the stories with predictive work. This has not been done on the page because of a wish to preserve the integrity of the stories as far as possible, by keeping them 'whole'.

As with all the activities in this book, the pre-reading tasks are meant as suggestions only. Often opportunities will arise because of what teachers and learners know about one another to make the lead-in phase much more group-specific and to involve learners more deeply. Learners in Spain, for example, will react differently to *Old Man at the Bridge* from learners in Colombia, who in turn will respond differently to *Heat*, given their closer experience of volcanoes.

Actual reading

Where possible, the reading should be done at one sitting, preferably outside class time. For example, pre-reading activities could be done in the second half of a lesson to encourage learners to read the whole story in private study or at home. Although a glossary has been provided for each story, learners should be encouraged to read for general sense and not to worry about detailed meaning at this stage. Some learners may want to use a dictionary while reading. It is worth pointing out to them that to look up words constantly will interrupt the flow of their reading, and that plenty can be understood without reference to a dictionary. It may also help if teachers give a time limit for reading (e.g. 10–15 minutes or less).

The initial comprehension exercises focus on main points, and learners can be asked to try to answer the questions immediately after or while reading. More detailed comprehension problems can be dealt with in the later vocabulary comprehension exercise.

If reading is done in the lesson, a possible approach is to divide the class into three or four groups, giving each group a different section of the story to read ('you read from line 1 to 40, you from 41 to 80...' and so on). After a few minutes learners regroup and try to work out what the whole story is by pooling their understanding of what they have read. Of course, it is important to divide up the story into coherent chunks, and to ensure that at some stage there is an opportunity for all learners to read the whole story. Alternatively, the cassette may be used (see below). I have included in the introduction to each story and the glossary some cultural points, but only teachers will know precisely what other cultural barriers might arise between writer and learner.

Comprehension work

The comprehension exercises immediately following the stories vary in style. The instruction at the beginning of each such exercise does not specify oral or written answers, allowing the teacher to decide when and how they wish learners to deal with the questions. Suggested answers are included in the key at the back for reference. However, whether they are true/false, multiple choice or 'open' questions, it is usually profitable to encourage learners to check answers together, and to discuss what in the story made them decide on that answer. So the following procedure is recommended:

a) individuals read the story (outside class) and try to answer the questions
b) pairs or groups of three compare their answers, justifying them by reference to the story and doing together any they were unable to do alone
c) the teacher elicits answers from groups, asking for reasons in each case

A popular activity to complement this is for individual learners to write down their own comprehension questions while reading. Each learner then finds someone to exchange his or her questions with, and they try to answer each others' questions. The question-setter must of course be able to answer his or her own questions! The teacher can use this as an opportunity to help learners rectify any problems they may have with question forms, while learners check one anothers' answers and help with comprehension problems while doing so.

Perhaps the most effective way to find out if learners have understood the key points of a story is to get them to retell the story briefly (possibly in their own language), orally or in writing. This is particularly successful if another group of learners can be found for them to exchange stories with, or if two halves of the class are reading different stories at the same time.

Detailed comprehension work

These multiple choice exercises aim to increase learners' ability to use the context to understand unfamiliar words and phrases. Again, allowing learners to do the exercises in pairs will generate useful discussion and allow them to help each other on a 'two-heads-are-better-than-one' basis. Work on meaning is sometimes interspersed with questions about use of vocabulary: learners have to identify or guess which of three or four uses offered are possible (normally more than one). As the examples are decontexualised, it will be helpful if further examples can be elicited/provided.

Writing exercises

These exercises are suggestions for follow-up writing, offering opportunities for creativity. The level of challenge has deliberately been kept moderate, to enable less able learners to go back to the story and base their writing on what happened in it as they recast events in a short letter from one of the protagonists, a diary entry etc. Learners can of course be as ambitious as they wish. However, various sorts of other more challenging written work can be set in addition. One of the most popular is the 'alternative ending' exercise (see *A High Dive* Ex.9); the teacher specifies a suitable point in the story and asks learners to finish the story from this point on in a way different from the one chosen by the author. Learners can also be asked to use the story as a stimulus for a story of their own, either based on real experiences or on imagination. Perhaps hardest of all is a written task that involves appreciation of, and personal reactions to, the story. This can be particularly rewarding if time is provided for oral preparation, perhaps after the exercises on style (see below).

Discussion exercises

The suggested procedure with these is:

a) a short time for individual reflection (and possibly note making)
b) discussion in pairs or small groups (5–10 minutes)
c) the teacher chairs a class discussion asking groups to report their opinions and encouraging further exchanges of ideas among groups
d) a 'vote' to end with (i.e. 'How many people think X and how many think Y?')

Style exercises

These simple exercises aim to raise learners' awareness of the way writers select language and style to achieve certain effects. They concentrate on features of the author's writing that learners can identify without too much difficulty. Usually one or two examples of a feature such as repetition (*Old Man at the Bridge* Ex.10) are given and learners are asked to find a few more. They then explore the reasons behind the feature and, if possible, say whether they find it successful. Suggested answers are provided in the key, but further examples may of course be found and other explanations are possible. Some teachers will want to go into the style of the story, and perhaps the way in which the story is structured, in much more detail than others.

The cassette

If you have access to appropriate equipment, the cassette, containing readings of selected stories, provides a useful aid.

a) If reading has to be done in lesson time, getting learners to listen and read simultaneously can ensure that all finish the story at the same time. Some teachers may prefer to have students start by listening only to make comprehension more challenging. Use of the cassette also allows the teacher to 'interrupt' the story at any time and to do comprehension checking and prediction work if he or she wishes to.

b) If learners have read the story at home, listening to it in class together (preferably without reading at the same time) towards the end of the series of exercises can throw interesting new light on the story.

c) The cassette is also very useful in self-access work (see 'To the Student' below).

d) The stories are read by different speakers with different accents roughly corresponding to the part of the world the story comes from. This should be exploited where possible to underline the notions of language variety and the status of English as a world language and the common property of many peoples beside the British, North Americans and Australasians.

The key and self-access work

Answers or suggested answers to all the exercises which are marked (K) are provided in the key at the back of the book, so that learners can use the book independently. The other exercises are also accessible for those working alone; however a comparison of ideas and reactions with teachers or other students would be fruitful.

TO THE STUDENT

The aim of this book is to provide short stories in English for people who are learning the language to enjoy, together with exercises to help them understand and learn more from the texts.

The book contains twelve complete and unsimplified short stories written in English by authors from many different countries in the world. They have been chosen because they are good examples of stories from the English-speaking world (not just from the USA and Britain). They are all short enough to be read in fifteen minutes or so, but most of them are about quite serious matters, and they will all make you think. Although some stories are more difficult than others, students at intermediate level and above will find them equally approachable and enjoyable, provided that they do not try to understand every word. They can be read in any order.

Before each story there are some exercises to make you think a little about some of the story's topics and to introduce you to some of the vocabulary (or to remind you of it if you know it already). It is best to do these exercises and look at the pictures with a friend, but if that is not possible, it will help you to write down some notes and ideas.

After you have done the introductory exercises and thought about the pictures, read the story in the way you would read a story in your own language. However, the first time you read a story in English, you should definitely not expect to (or try to) understand every word; stories are meant to be read for interest and pleasure, and using a dictionary all the time will not give you this. In fact, worrying about what a new word means may distract you from the main idea of the story. Instead, keep on reading, trying to work out the meaning of new words from what you know about the story already and from the words you do know. You can use a dictionary later, after trying the vocabulary exercises.

The cassette

A cassette containing readings of selected stories is available for use with this book. If you find it easier, you may prefer to listen to the cassette at the same time as you read. However, it would be much better to read the story through first, quickly trying to answer the questions as you read, and then to listen to the cassette later. Or, if you prefer listening to stories, try listening *only* before listening and reading at the same time.

The key

Answers and suggested answers to all the exercises marked Ⓚ are in the key at the back of the book. You can work on the exercises alone and then look at the key when you finish each one. The other exercises do not have simple answers, but you can try to do them anyway. This will be much more successful if you can find a friend to work with, to show your written exercises to, and to discuss your ideas about the stories with.

If you enjoy these stories, try to read others, and perhaps novels too, by the same writers.

1 The First Day of School

by William Saroyan

Ⓚ **Exercise 1**   Look at the list of adjectives below. Discuss them with a partner and together put them into three groups; Positive, Negative and Either.

frightened   happy   shy   excited   angry
sad   upset   proud   worried   delighted

Positive (good)	Negative (bad)	Either (not sure)

Exercise 2   a) Can you remember your first day at school, or at a new school? Select adjectives from the list above (and others) to describe your feelings. If you can't remember, try to imagine yourself at the age of five going to school for the first time.
b) What did you particularly like about life at primary/junior school? What did you particularly dislike? You may want to talk about the following:

other pupils, teachers, different kinds of lesson, breaktime (recess), the school building, classrooms and playground (yard), the furniture, the head teacher etc.

Then discuss your likes and dislikes with someone else.

Exercise 3
Look at the two photographs. With a partner invent a story in which the two are related.

This story is set in a city in the USA. The boy in the story is very young and has never been to school before.

The First Day of School

He was a little boy named Jim, the first and only child of Dr Louis Davy, 717 Mattei Building, and it was his first day at school. His father was French, a small heavy-set man of forty whose boyhood had been full of poverty and unhappiness and ambition. His mother
5 was dead: she died when Jim was born, and the only woman he knew intimately was Amy, the Swedish housekeeper.

It was Amy who dressed him in his Sunday clothes, and took him to school. Jim liked Amy, but he didn't like her for taking him to school. He told her so. All the way to school he told her so.
10 I don't like you, he said. I don't like you any more.

I like *you*, the housekeeper said.

Then why are you taking me to school? he said.

He had taken walks with Amy before, once all the way to the Court House Park for the Sunday afternoon band concert, but this
15 walk to school was different.

What for? he said.

Everybody must go to school, the housekeeper said.

Did you go to school? he said.

No, said Amy.
20 Then why do I have to go? he said.

You will like it, said the housekeeper.

He walked on with her in silence, holding her hand. I don't like you, he said. I don't like you any more.

I like you, said Amy.

25 Then why are you taking me to school? he said again.

Why?

The housekeeper knew how frightened a little boy could be about going to school.

You will like it, she said. I think you will sing songs and play
30 games.

I don't want to, he said.

I will come and get you every afternoon, she said.

I don't like you, he told her again.

She felt very unhappy about the little boy going to school, but she
35 knew that he would have to go.

The school building was very ugly to her and to the boy. She didn't like the way it made her feel, and going up the steps with him she wished he didn't have to go to school. The halls and rooms scared her, and him, and the smell of the place too. And he didn't
40 like Mr Barber, the principal.

Amy despised Mr Barber.

What is the name of your son? Mr Barber said.

This is Dr Louis Davy's son, said Amy. His name is Jim. I am Dr Davy's housekeeper.

45 James? said Mr Barber.

Not James, said Amy, just Jim.

All right, said Mr Barber. Any middle name?

No, said Amy. He is too small for a middle name. Just Jim Davy.

All right, said Mr Barber. We'll try him out in the first grade. If
50 he doesn't get along all right we'll try him out in kindergarten.

Dr Davy said to start him in the first grade, said Amy. Not kindergarten.

All right, said Mr Barber.

The housekeeper knew how frightened the little boy was, sitting
55 on the chair, and she tried to let him know how much she loved him and how sorry she was about everything. She wanted to say something fine to him about everything, but she couldn't say anything, and she was very proud of the nice way he got down from the chair and stood beside Mr Barber, waiting to go with him to a classroom.

60 On the way home she was so proud of him she began to cry.

Miss Binney, the teacher of the first grade, was an old lady who was all dried out. The room was full of little boys and girls. School smelled strange and sad. He sat at a desk and listened carefully.

He heard some of the names: *Charles, Ernest, Alvin, Norman,*
65 *Betty, Hannah, Juliet, Viola, Polly.*

He listened carefully and heard Miss Binney say, Hannah Winter, what *are* you chewing? And he saw Hannah Winter blush. He liked Hannah Winter right from the beginning.

Gum, said Hannah.

70 Put it in the waste-basket, said Miss Binney.

He saw the little girl walk to the front of the class, take the gum from her mouth, and drop it into the waste-basket.

And he heard Miss Binney say, Ernest Gaskin, what are *you* chewing?

Glossary

despised (*l.41*): thought very
badly of

first grade (*l.49*): the first year
in primary (grade) school in
the USA

kindergarten (*l.50*): a class or
school for children younger
than first grade (i.e. under
six)

dried out (*l.62*): wrinkled and
tired

75   Gum, said Ernest.

And he liked Ernest Gaskin too.

They met in the schoolyard, and Ernest taught him a few jokes.

Amy was in the hall when school ended. She was sullen and angry at everybody until she saw the little boy. She was amazed that he
80 wasn't changed, that he wasn't hurt, or perhaps utterly unalive, murdered. The school and everything about it frightened her very much. She took his hand and walked out of the building with him, feeling angry and proud.

Jim said. What comes after twenty-nine?
85   Thirty, said Amy.

Your face is dirty, he said.

His father was very quiet at the supper table.

What comes after twenty-nine? the boy said.

Thirty, said his father.
90   Your face is dirty, he said.

In the morning he asked his father for a nickel.

What do you want a nickel for? his father said.

Gum, he said.

His father gave him a nickel and on the way to school he stopped
95 at Mrs Riley's store and bought a package of Spearmint.

Do you want a piece? he asked Amy.

Do you want to give me a piece? the housekeeper said.

Jim thought about it a moment, and then he said, Yes.

Do you like me? said the housekeeper.
100   I like you, said Jim. Do you like me?

Yes, said the housekeeper.

Do you like school?

Jim didn't know for sure, but he knew he liked the part about gum. And Hannah Winter. And Ernest Gaskin.
105   I don't know, he said.

Do you sing? asked the housekeeper.

No, we don't sing, he said.

Do you play games? she said.

Not in the school, he said. In the yard we do.
110   He liked the part about gum very much.

Miss Binney said, Jim Davy, what are you *chewing*?

Ha ha ha, he thought.

Gum, he said.

He walked to the waste-paper basket and back to his seat, and
115 Hannah Winter saw him, and Ernest Gaskin too. That was the best part of school.

It began to grow too.

Ernest Gaskin, he shouted in the schoolyard, *what* are you *chewing*?
120   Raw elephant meat, said Ernest Gaskin. Jim Davy, what are *you* chewing?

Jim tried to think of something very funny to be chewing, but he couldn't.

Gum, he said, and Ernest Gaskin laughed louder than Jim
125 laughed when Ernest Gaskin said raw elephant meat.

sullen (l.78): in a bad mood, unhappy
unalive (l.80): dead, or feeling dead
nickel (l.91): a five cent coin (100 cents = 1 dollar)
raw (l.120): not cooked (Ernest is making a joke)

It was funny no matter what you said.

Going back to the classroom Jim saw Hannah Winter in the hall.

Hannah Winter, he said, *what in the world* are you *chewing*?

The little girl was startled. She wanted to say something nice that
130 would honestly show how nice she felt about having Jim say her
name and ask her the funny question, making fun of school, but she
couldn't think of anything that nice to say because they were almost
in the room and there wasn't time enough.

Tutti-frutti, she said with desperate haste.

135 It seemed to Jim he had never before heard such a glorious word,
and he kept repeating the word to himself all day.

Tutti-frutti, he said to Amy on the way home.

Amy Larson, he said, *what, are, you, chewing*?

He told his father all about it at the supper table.

140 He said, Once there was a hill. On the hill there was a mill.
Under the mill there was a walk. Under the walk there was a key.
What is it?

I don't know, his father said. What is it?

Milwaukee, said the boy.

145 The housekeeper was delighted.

Mill. Walk. Key, Jim said.

Tutti-frutti.

What's that? said his father.

Gum, he said. The kind Hannah Winter chews.

150 Who's Hannah Winter? said his father.

She's in my room, he said.

Oh, said his father.

After supper he sat on the floor with the small red and blue and
yellow top that hummed while it spinned. It was all right, he
155 guessed. It was still very sad, but the gum part of it was very funny
and the Hannah Winter part very nice. Raw elephant meat, he
thought with great inward delight.

Raw elephant meat, he said aloud to his father who was reading
the evening paper. His father folded the paper and sat on the floor
160 beside him. The housekeeper saw them together on the floor and
for some reason tears came to her eyes.

startled (*l.129*): surprised
tutti frutti (*l.134*): an Italian
    ice cream flavour (fruit)
Milwaukee (*l.144*): a city in
    the US State of Wisconsin
my room (*l.151*): my class
top (*l.154*): a child's toy
hummed (*l.154*): the noise
    some tops make
spinned (*l.154*): a top
    balances upright and goes
    round very fast, or spins

Ⓚ **Exercise 4**   **Are the following statements about the story** *true* **or** *false*? **If there
isn't enough information in the story, write** *don't know*.

a) Jim didn't like Amy at all.

b) Amy never went to school herself.

c) Amy thought it was cruel to send Jim to school.

d) Neither Amy nor Jim liked the atmosphere of the school.

e) Jim's father wanted him to begin in the kindergarten.

f) Amy wished Jim were her own son.

15

Ⓚ **Exercise 5**   **Answer the following.**

a) What did Jim like about life at school? (Mention two or three things.)
b) Why was Amy surprised when she saw Jim at the end of his first day at school?
c) Why did Jim ask his father for money?
d) What did Jim learn on his first day at school?
e) How did Jim behave with his father that evening?

Ⓚ **Exercise 6**   **Find these phrases in the story, and notice the way in which they are used. In each case circle a), b) or c) to show which you think is the best equivalent. Show which examples are correct in the same way. Of these, usually at least two are correct.**

1 'heavy-set man' (*line 3*)
    a) a fat man
    b) a man with broad shoulders and a strong build
    c) a very serious man

2 'knew intimately' (*line 6*)
    a) knew very well
    b) thought she was his mother
    c) knew quite well

3 'Swedish housekeeper' (*line 6*)
    a) stepmother
    b) a nanny who looks after children
    c) a woman from Sweden who was paid to look after the home

4 'the halls and rooms scared her' (*line 38*)
    a) the school made her feel unhappy
    b) the school building frightened her
    c) it reminded her of her own happier school days

5 'she was very proud of the nice way he . . .' (*line 58*)
    a) she admired the way Jim behaved
    b) she thought Jim was a nice child
    c) she was surprised by Jim's good behaviour

6 Which of these are correct:
    a) She felt proud of herself.
    b) I am proud of my new bicycle.
    c) He looks proudly this morning.

7 'what *are* you chewing?' (*line 67*)

Miss Binney was angry because
a) Hannah couldn't answer
b) Hannah had something in her mouth
c) Hannah was talking to a friend

8 Which of these are correct:

a) John blushed because he was hot.
b) I was so embarrassed by what she said that I blushed.
c) Why are you blushing?

9 'Your face is dirty' (*line 90*)

Jim said this because
a) he was angry with his father
b) he was making a joke with words that sound the same
c) he wanted his father to wash

10 'with desperate haste' (*line 134*)

a) in an unhappy way
b) very angry with Jim
c) very quickly, in a great hurry

11 'with great inward delight' (*line 157*)

a) feeling very happy inside
b) with a feeling of disgust in his stomach
c) not showing his feelings

Ⓚ **Exercise 7**

Here are some adjectives used in the story, with some prepositions which can be used after them.

frightened (of)   proud (of)
sorry (for)   amazed (about, at)
scared (of)   sad (about)
upset (about, with)   startled (by)
unhappy (about, with)   excited (about)
angry (about, with)   delighted (with)

Use these adjectives to describe how Jim and Amy felt at the following times during the first day at school (some only apply to Jim).

● on the way to school
● arriving at the school building
● talking to Mr Barber
● in class
● in the school yard
● just after school
● at home in the evening

Exercise 8

Write a letter from Amy to an American friend of hers living in New York. Her friend visited her last Christmas and met Jim. In the letter, written on the evening of the day described in the story, Amy explains how she felt. Begin like this.

> 435 W. 18th Street
> New Orleans, La.
> 2 September

Dear Mary Lou,

Thank you for your nice long letter, which I received last Friday. It is good to hear that your new job is interesting, and that you have a kind boss at last! I'm sure you'll do very well.

I must tell you about the day I've just had with Jim. As you know, he has reached school age now. He wasn't looking forward to starting school at all, and I wasn't looking forward to taking him . . .

Exercise 9

Think about the following questions carefully. Then compare your answers with a partner's.
a) What do you think of the story? Were your feelings on the first day of school similar to Jim's or different?
b) Why do you think Amy started to cry at the end of the story?
c) Imagine what you would feel or remember what you felt in the following situations.

- first plane trip
- winning a competition
- going to the dentist
- failing an important test
- getting married
- hearing strange noises in an old house at night

About the Author

William Saroyan (1908–1981) was born and always had a home in Fresno, California, although he moved to Paris in 1958 for tax reasons. He left school when he was only fifteen and educated himself by reading and writing. His first collection of stories, *The Daring Young Man on the Flying Trapeze* (1936), was very popular because it emphasised the joy of living in spite of the poverty and unemployment of the time. From that time until his death, Saroyan wrote many amusing stories, novels and plays, often about family life and the way in which people are basically good-natured.

2 Tell Us About the Turkey, Jo

by Alan Marshall

Ⓚ **Exercise 1** **Label the drawing with the following words.**

nose
scalp
stomach
shoulder
knee
forehead
neck
chest
wrist
ankle
lips
chin
back
thumb
toes

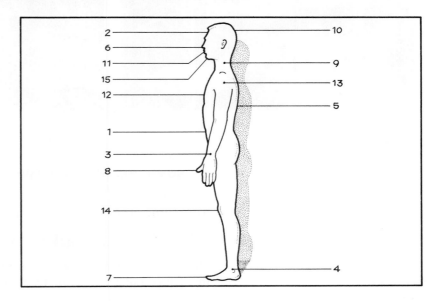

Exercise 2 **Look at the following list of accidents. Circle the ones that have happened to you. Then put the numbers 1 to 5 beside the most unpleasant and dangerous ones (1 = the most horrible).**

Falling	off a bicycle	Breaking	an arm
	off a horse		a leg
	down the stairs		your neck
	into a river		
		Being bitten	by a snake
Burning	your hand		by a large dog
	your hair		
		Being stung	by a bee
Cutting	your head		by a jelly fish
	your foot		
	your wrist	Being chased	by a bull

Compare your answers with a partner's. Tell him or her about any accidents that have happened to you. Which do you remember most clearly? Why?

19

Exercise 3   Look at the photographs. With a partner invent a story in which they are related.

This story is set in Victoria, South Australia, near the city of Melbourne. The children in it, and the narrator, are Australians.

Tell Us About the Turkey, Jo

He came walking though the rusty grasses and sea-weedish plants that fringe Lake Corangamite. Behind him strode his brother.

He was very fair. His hair was a pale gold and when he scratched his head the parted hairs revealed the pink skin of his scalp. His
5   eyes were very blue. He was freckled. His nose was tipped upward. I liked him tremendously. I judged him to be about four and a half years old and his brother twice that age.

They wore blue overalls and carried them jauntily. The clean wind came across the water and fluttered the material against their
10   legs. Their air was one of independence and release from authority.

They scared the two plovers I had been watching. The birds lifted with startled cries and banked against the wind. They cut across large clouds patched with blue and sped away, flapping low over the water.

15   The two boys and I exchanged greetings while we looked each other over. I think they liked me. The little one asked me several personal questions. He wanted to know what I was doing there, why I was wearing a green shirt, where was my mother? I gave him the information with the respect due to another seeker of knowledge. I
20   then asked him a question and thus learned of the dangers and disasters that had beset his path.

'How did you get that cut on your head?' I asked. In the centre of his forehead a pink scar divided his freckles.

Glossary

fringe lake Corangamite (l.2): grow round the edge of the lake
strode (l.2): walked with big steps
freckled (l.5): he had little brown marks on his face, perhaps because of the sun
jauntily (l.8): in a cheerful and confident way
plover (l.11): a kind of bird
scar (l.23): a mark left after an injury

20

The little boy looked quickly at his brother. The brother
answered for him. The little boy expected and conceded this. He
looked at the brother expectantly and, as the brother spoke, the
little boy's eyes shone, his lips parted, as one who listens to a
thrilling story.

'He fell off a baby's chair when he was little,' said the brother.
'He hit his head on a shovel and bled over it.'

'Ye-e-s,' faltered the little boy, awed by the picture, and in his
eyes was the excitement and the thrill of danger passed. He looked
across the flat water, rapt in the thought of the chair and the shovel
and the blood.

'A cow kicked him once,' said the brother.

'A cow!' I exclaimed.

'Yes,' he said.

'Go on, Jo,' said the little boy eagerly, standing before him and
looking up into his face.

'He tried to leg-rope it,' Jo explained, 'and the cow let out and
got him in the stomach.'

'In the stomach,' emphasized the little boy turning quickly to me
and nodding his head.

'Gee!' I exclaimed.

'Gee!' echoed the little boy.

'It winded him,' said Jo.

'I was winded,' said the little boy slowly as if in doubt. 'What's
winded, Jo?'

'He couldn't breathe properly,' Jo addressed me.

'I couldn't breathe a bit,' said the little boy.

'That was bad,' I said.

'Yes, it was bad, wasn't it, Jo?' said the little boy.

'Yes,' said Jo.

Jo looked intently at the little boy as if searching for scars of other
conflicts.

'A ladder fell on him once,' he said.

The little boy looked quickly at my face to see if I was impressed.
The statement had impressed him very much.

'No,' said I unbelievingly.

'Will I show him, Jo?' asked the little boy eagerly.

'Yes,' said Jo.

The little boy, after giving me a quick glance of satisfaction, bent
and placed his hands on his knees. Jo lifted the back of his brother's
shirt collar and peered into the warm shadow between his back and
the cotton material.

'You can see it,' he said uncertainly, searching the white skin for
its whereabouts.

The little boy twisted his arm behind his back and strove to touch
a spot on one of his shoulders.

'It's there, Jo. Can you see it, Jo?'

'Yes. That's it,' said Jo. 'You come here and see.' He looked at
me. 'Don't move, Jimmy.'

'Jo's found it,' announced Jimmy, his head twisted to face me.

I rose from my seat on a pitted rock nestling in grass and stepped

shovel (*l.30*): a tool for
  digging
faltered (*l.31*): spoke in a
  hesitant way
awed (*l.31*): impressed
winded (*l.46*): hit in the
  stomach so that he lost his
  breath for a few moments
collar (*l.64*): the neck of a
  shirt or jacket etc.
strove (*l.68*): tried hard
  (present: strive)

75 over to them. I bent and looked beneath the lifted collar. On the white skin of his shoulder was the smooth ridge of a small scar.

'Yes, it's there all right,' I said. 'I'll bet you cried when you got that.'

The little boy turned to Jo. 'Did I cry, Jo?'

80 'A bit,' said Jo.

'I never do cry much, do I, Jo?'

'No,' said Jo.

'How did it happen?' I asked.

'The ladder had hooks in it . . .' commenced Jo.

85 'Had hooks in it,' emphasized the little boy nodding at me.

'And he pulled it down on top of him,' continued Jo.

'Oo!' said the little boy excitedly, clasping his hands and holding them between his knees while he stamped his feet. 'Oo-o-o.'

'It knocked him rotten,' said Jo.

90 'I was knocked rotten,' declared the little boy slowly as if revealing the fact to himself for the first time.

There was a pause while the little boy enjoyed his thoughts.

'It's a nice day, isn't it?' Jo sought new contacts with me.

'Yes,' said I.

95 The little boy stood in front of his brother, entreating him with his eyes.

'What else was I in, Jo?' he pleaded.

Jo pondered, looking at the ground and nibbling his thumb.

'You was in nothin' else,' he said, finally.

100 'Aw, Jo!' The little boy was distressed at the finality of the statement. He bent suddenly and pulled up the leg of his overalls. He searched his bare leg for marks of violence.

'What's that, Jo?' He pointed to a faint mark on his knee.

'That's nothin',' said Jo. Jo wanted to talk about ferrets. 'You

105 know, ferrets . . .' he began.

'It looks like something,' I said, looking closely at the mark.

Jo leant forward and examined it. The little boy, clutching the crumpled leg of his trousers, looked from my face to his brother's and back again, anxiously waiting a decision.

110 Jo made a closer examination, rubbing the mark with his finger. The little boy followed Jo's investigation with an expectant attention.

'You mighta had a burn once. I don't know.'

'I wish I did have a burn, Jo,' said the little boy. It was a plea for

115 a commitment from Jo, but Jo was a stickler for truth.

'I can't remember you being burnt,' he said. 'Mum'd know.'

'Perhaps you can think of another exciting thing,' I suggested.

'Yes,' said the little boy eagerly. He came over and took my hand so that we might await together the result of Jo's cogitation. He

120 looked up at me and said, 'Isn't Jo good?'

'Very good,' I said.

'He knows about me and everything.'

'Yes,' I said.

There was a faint 'Hulloo' from behind us. We all turned. A little

125 girl came running through the rocks in the barrier that guards the

knocked him rotten (*l.89*): knocked him unconscious

pondered (*l.98*): thought deeply

nibbling (*l.98*): biting

ferrets (*l.104*): small animals used for hunting rabbits

stickler for truth (*l.115*): Jo insisted on telling only true stories

lake from the cultivated lands. She had thin legs and wore long, black stockings. One had come loose from its garter and, as she ran, she bent and pulled and strove to push its top beneath the elastic band. Her gait was thus a series of hops and unequal strides.

130 She called her brothers' names as she ran and in her voice was the note of the bearer-of-news.

'Dad must be home,' said Jo.

But the little boy was resentful of this intrusion. 'What does she want?' he said sourly.

135 The little girl had reached a flat stretch of grass and her speed had increased. Her short hair fluttered in the wind of her running.

She waved a hand. 'We have a new baby sister,' she yelled.

'Aw, pooh!' exclaimed the little boy.

He turned and tugged at Jo's arm. 'Have you thought of anything

140 exciting yet, Jo?' His face lit to a sudden recollection. 'Tell him how I got chased by the turkey,' he cried.

garter (*l.127*): a band round her legs to keep her stocking up
sourly (*l.134*): angrily

Ⓚ **Exercise 4**   **According to the story, which of the following complete the sentence best?**

1 The narrator met the boys
   a) at their house
   b) near a lake
   c) on the beach

2 Jo was
   a) older than his brother, Jimmy
   b) younger than Jimmy
   c) the same age as Jimmy

3 Jimmy didn't tell the stories himself because
   a) he was too shy
   b) he couldn't remember
   c) he preferred to hear Jo tell them

4 Jo stopped talking about Jimmy's accidents because
   a) he wanted to talk about something else
   b) there was nothing else to say
   c) he was angry with Jimmy

5 When his sister came with her news, Jimmy was
   a) very excited
   b) not at all interested
   c) horrified

Ⓚ **Exercise 5**　Read the story again quickly to complete the following table about Jimmy's accidents.

Accident	Result
he fell off a baby's chair	_____
_____	he was winded in the stomach
_____	he was knocked unconscious

Ⓚ **Exercise 6**　Find these phrases in the story, and notice the way in which they are used. In each case circle a), b) or c) to show which you think is the best equivalent. Show which examples are correct in the same way. Of these, usually at least two are correct.

1 'sea-weedish plants' (*line 1*)
   a) plants that grow in the sea
   b) plants similar to the ones that can be found in the sea
   c) plants looking like a dish

2 'he was very fair' (*line 3*)
   a) he had blond hair and light skin
   b) he was a very nice-looking boy
   c) he looked honest and kind

3 Which of these are correct:
   a) She has long, fair hair.
   b) That's not fair; you cheated.
   c) He looks fairly.

4 'their air was . . .' (*line 10*)
   a) they smelled like free animals
   b) the way they behaved was independent
   c) they breathed in an independent way

5 'release from authority' (*line 10*)
   a) nobody was around to give them orders
   b) as if they had come out of prison
   c) as if they had never been under anyone's authority

6 Which of these are correct:
   a) The terrorists released the hostages.
   b) The prisoner had a release.
   c) The teacher released her class early.

24

7 'a thrilling story' (*line 28*)

    a) a very exciting story
    b) a murder story
    c) an adventure story

8 Which of these are correct:

    a) I am thrilling after that film.
    b) He likes reading thrillers.
    c) They had a thrilling adventure.

9 'rapt in the thought' (*line 33*)

    a) horrified by the idea
    b) thinking about it for the first time
    c) lost in thought

10 'He tried to leg-rope it' (*line 40*)

    a) he tried to ride it.
    b) he tried to catch it by putting a cord round its legs
    c) he tried to tie its legs together

11 'its whereabouts' (*line 67*)

    a) the position of the injury
    b) the position of the collar
    c) the place where the shadow was

12 'entreating him with his eyes' (*line 95*)

    a) looking at him angrily
    b) asking him with his eyes to continue
    c) admiring him a lot

Ⓚ Exercise 7

a) Match the adjectives on the left with their opposites on the right.

proud	depressed
excited	reluctant
cheerful	modest
eager	bored

b) Make opposites of these adjectives using un- or dis-.

_____happy   _____sure   _____impressed
_____satisfied   _____interested

Which words describe Jimmy's attitude as he listens to Jo talking about him?

Exercise 8

Discuss the following questions with a partner.

- Why did the author like the two boys? Would you have liked them?
- What differences are there between these Australian boys' lives and the lives of similar boys in your country?
- What were the differences between the two brothers? Were they mainly because of difference in age?
- Do you have a brother or sister? What differences were there between you when you were young children? What differences are there now?
- What are the main advantages or disadvantages of having younger and older brothers or sisters?
- Did you find the story amusing? If so, why?

Exercise 9

Imagine the story was being written as a paragraph in an autobiography written by Jo 50 years later. Begin like this.

. . . I was walking along the bank of Lake Corangamite with my little brother, Jimmy, one day when we met a stranger. The man was very friendly, and Jimmy started a conversation with him. It was fine until the man started asking Jimmy about the scars he had at the time . . .

Ⓚ Exercise 10

The author gives a clear idea of Jimmy's feelings in the story by describing the way he looked. For example, *line 25* **'He looked at the brother expectantly . . . the little boy's eyes shone, his lips parted . . .'. Find at least four other phrases where the author does this. How does the description in each case help us understand the mood of the child? What do you think of the way the author does this?**

About the Author

Alan Marshall was born in a country area of Victoria, South Australia in 1902. His most famous book was written in 1955. It is called *I Can Jump Puddles*, and is about a boy with polio growing up in this part of Australia. It describes Marshall's own childhood and was followed by other autobiographical books. Alan Marshall has also written a large number of short stories, and this is a good example.

3 Heat

by Jean Rhys

Ⓚ **Exercise 1**   **Which of the words on the right do you associate with the natural disasters on the left?**

volcano	high wind
	flames
tidal wave	ash
	lava
earthquake	floods
	smoke and fumes
hurricane	falling buildings
	cars turned over
landslide/avalanche	cracks in the earth
	digging for people
forest fire/bush fire	black clouds
	burnt crops and houses

Exercise 2   **Which of the above natural disasters would you be most afraid of? Why? Tell your partner about a natural disaster you have heard about (or been involved in).**

Exercise 3   **Look at the two photographs. With a partner, invent a story in which they are related.**

This story is set on the island of Dominica in the Caribbean, where the writer was born. As you can see from the map below, the islands in this part of the Caribbean are quite small and close together.

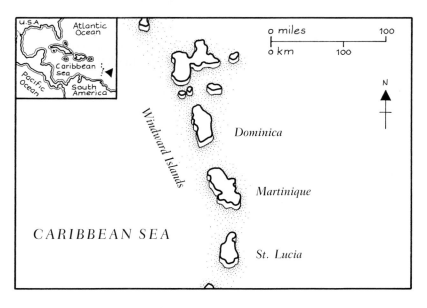

Heat

Ash had fallen. Perhaps it had fallen the night before or perhaps it was still falling. I can only remember in patches. I was looking at it two feet deep on the flat roof outside my bedroom. The ash and the silence. Nobody talked in the street, nobody talked while we ate, or
5 hardly at all. I know now that they were all frightened. They thought our volcano was going up.

Our volcano was called the boiling lake. That's what it was, a sheet of water that always boiled. From what fires? I thought of it as a mysterious place that few people had ever seen. In the churchyard
10 where we often went – for death was not then a taboo subject – quite near the grave of my little sister, was a large marble head-stone. 'Sacred to the memory of Clive __, who lost his life at the boiling lake in Dominica in an heroic attempt to save his guide'. Aged twenty-seven. I remember that too.
15 He was a young Englishman, a visitor, who had gone exploring with two guides to the boiling lake. As they were standing looking at it one of the guides, who was a long way ahead, staggered and fell. The other seized hold of the Englishman's hand and said 'Run!' There must have been some local tradition that poisonous gases
20 sometimes came out of the lake. After a few steps the Englishman pulled his hand away and went back and lifted up the man who had fallen. Then he too staggered and they both fell. The surviving guide ran and told what had happened.

In the afternoon two little friends were coming to see us and to

Glossary

taboo subject (*l.10*): a subject not to be talked about
seized hold of (*l.18*): took hold of quickly with force

28

my surprise they both arrived carrying large glass bottles. Both the bottles had carefully written labels pasted on: 'Ash collected from the streets of Roseau on May 8th, 1902.' The little boy asked me if I'd like to have his jar, but I refused. I didn't want to touch the ash. I don't remember the rest of the day. I must have gone to bed, for

30 that night my mother woke me and without saying anything, led me to the window. There was a huge black cloud over Martinique. I couldn't ever describe that cloud, so huge and black it was, but I have never forgotten it. There was no moon, no stars, but the edges of the cloud were flame-coloured and in the middle what looked to

35 me like lightning flickered, never stopping. My mother said: 'You will never see anything like this in your life again.' That was all. I must have gone to sleep at the window and been carried to bed.

Next morning we heard what had happened. Was it a blue or a grey day? I only know ash wasn't falling any longer. The Roseau

40 fishermen went out very early, as they did in those days. They met the fishermen from Port de France, who knew. That was how we heard before the cablegrams, the papers and all the rest came flooding in. That was how we heard of Mont Pelée's eruption and the deaths of 40,000 people, and that there was nothing left of St

45 Pierre.

As soon as ships were sailing again between Dominica and Martinique my father went to see the desolation that was left. He brought back a pair of candlesticks, tall heavy brass candlesticks which must have been in a church. The heat had twisted them into

50 an extraordinary shape. He hung them on the wall of the dining-room and I stared at them all through meals, trying to make sense of the shape.

It was after this that the gossip started. That went on for years so I can remember it well. St Pierre, they said, was a very wicked city.

55 It had not only a theatre, but an opera house, which was probably wickeder still. Companies from Paris performed there. But worse than this was the behaviour of the women who were the prettiest in the West Indies. They tied their turbans in a particular way, a sort of language of love that all St Pierre people understood. Tied in one

60 way it meant 'I am in love, I am not free'; tied in another way it meant 'You are welcome, I am free'. Even the women who were married, or as good as, tied their kerchiefs in the 'I am free' way. And that wasn't all. The last bishop who had visited the city had taken off his shoes and solemnly shaken them over it. After that, of

65 course, you couldn't wonder.

As I grew older I heard of a book by a man called Lafcadio Hearn who had written about St Pierre as it used to be, about Ti Marie and all the others, but I never found the book and stopped looking for it. However, one day I did discover a pile of old newspapers and

70 magazines, some illustrated: the English version of the eruption. They said nothing about the opera house or the theatre which must have seemed to the English the height of frivolity in a Caribbean island, and very little about the city and its inhabitants. It was nearly all about the one man who had survived. He was a convict im-

75 prisoned in an underground cell, so he escaped – the only one out

lightning flickered (l.35): there was an electric storm nearby

cablegram (l.42): telegram

came flooding in (l.42): arrived in large numbers

candlesticks (l.48): holders for candles

gossip (l.53): talk about other people

companies (l.56): groups of actors, dancers etc.

kerchiefs (l.62): scarves worn round the head or neck

shoes ... solemnly shaken (l.64): a traditional way of showing you think a place is so bad that you will never return

you couldn't wonder (l.65): it wasn't surprising

height of frivolity (l.72): not at all serious

cell (l.75): a room in a prison

of 40,000. He was now travelling round the music-halls of the world being exhibited. They had taught him a little speech. He must be quite a rich man – what did he do with his money? Would he marry again? His wife and children had been killed in the eruption. . . . I

80   read all this then I thought but it wasn't like that, it wasn't like that at all.

Ⓚ **Exercise 4**   **Are the following statements about the story *true* or *false*. If there isn't sufficient information in the story, write *don't know*.**

a) There is a volcano on Dominica and another on Martinique.
b) The ash in Roseau came from Dominica.
c) The big black cloud was caused by the eruption.
d) The writer first heard about the destruction of St Pierre through her father.
e) Some people thought St Pierre had been destroyed because its inhabitants were bad people.
f) The English newspapers reported the catastrophe in detail.
g) The man who escaped was a singer.
h) If he hadn't been in prison he would probably have been killed.

Ⓚ **Exercise 5**   **Find these words and phrases in the story, and notice the way in which they are used. In each case circle a), b) or c) to show which one you think is the best equivalent. Show which examples are correct in the same way. Of these, usually at least two are correct.**

1 'I can only remember in patches' (*line 2*)
a) I don't have a good memory
b) my memory of the events isn't complete
c) I've forgotten almost everything

2 Which of these are correct:
a) She repaired her jeans with a patch.
b) He spoke in patches of English.
c) We drove through a patch of fog.

3 '. . . or hardly at all' (*line 4*)
a) they spoke but very little
b) they spoke in an unkind way
c) everybody kept silent

4 Which of these are correct:
a) Mrs White, my boss, works very hardly.
b) We hardly ate anything at all.
c) A:Do you play tennis? B:Hardly ever.

30

5 'a mysterious place' (*line 9*)
a) a horrible place
b) a secret and unknown place
c) a place that no one visited

6 'staggered' (*line 17*)
a) lost his balance
b) lost consciousness, blacked out
c) tripped over something lying on the ground

7 Which of these are correct:
a) The tree staggered and fell with a crash.
b) The man, who had drunk too much, staggered out of the room.
c) I was staggered to find out my sister was already married.

8 'wasn't falling any longer' (*line 39*)
a) had stopped falling
b) wasn't falling so thickly
c) had been falling for a long time

9 'a very wicked city' (*line 54*)
a) a very ugly place
b) a city full of bad people
c) a very enjoyable city

10 'a pile of old newspapers' (*line 69*)
a) several newspapers
b) a whole variety of news-papers
c) a lot of newspapers on top of each other

11 Which of these are correct:
a) There is a clothes pile in the cupboard.
b) He piled rice on her plate.
c) There were piles of rubbish in the street.

Ⓚ **Exercise 6** **In the following list, two different stories are mixed up. Write the numbers of the sentences in the correct box on page 32.**

1 A man went to explore a volcanic crater, which was full of hot water.
2 The man had been in prison for a long time.
3 The room where he lived was underground.
4 He went with two local people who knew the place well.
5 The volcano on the island erupted and everyone else in that town was killed.
6 One of the guides he was with slipped and fell into the crater.
7 He began to run, but then decided to go back to help his companion.

31

8 The man's family were killed in the disaster.

9 But he fell into the crater and was lost.

10 The other guide returned safely and told everyone what had happened.

11 After that, he made a lot of money telling people the story.

12 A memorial to him was put in the town cemetery, so people remembered him.

Happened in Martinique	Happened in Dominica

Ⓚ **Exercise 7** **The verbs on the left are all from the story. Match them with the complementations on the right.**

Verbs	Complements
stagger	someone's arm until they say 'Ouch!'
frighten	some milk in a saucepan
survive	at someone's strange clothes
seize	into a hospital feeling very ill
boil	why someone is late
refuse	a fall off a three-storey building
flicker	from a prison cell by digging a tunnel
flood	all the streets of a town near the river
twist	the money from the till and run away
stare	hands with someone
gossip	a child with ghost stories
tie	like a candle in the wind
shake	to wait for her any longer
wonder	a rope round his waist before climbing up
escape	about the neighbours

Exercise 8 **The story mentions an English newspaper. What kind of report appeared in the Dominica newspaper in the days following the eruption? Write a brief article, beginning as follows.**

CATASTROPHE ON MARTINIQUE

Following yesterday's fall of ash in Roseau, reports are now coming in from Martinique. A fisherman who visited Dominica yesterday said . . .

Exercise 9

Do you agree or disagree with the following? Mark your opinion. Then discuss with a partner.

- Natural disasters are 'acts of God'; there is nothing humans can do to avoid such catastrophes. _____
- Natural disasters help to remind people of the value of life and of their fellowship with one another. _____
- It would be absurd to ask people to move away from earthquake, volcano and flood areas; anyway, they prefer to put up with the risks. _____
- Much more money should be spent on earthquake and eruption forecasting. _____
- Natural disasters are insignificant when you consider man-made disasters such as wars, crimes, and drug abuse. _____

Ⓚ Exercise 10

In the story the writer mixes up the elements in the list below. Give an example of each (with line numbers).

- personal details referring to her own family _____
- information from gossip and legend _____
- things she read many years later _____
- her own memories _____

a) Why do you think the writer organises (disorganises?) the story in this way? What do you think of the effect she creates?

b) She also uses 'informal' language (e.g. *line 7* **'That's what it was . . .'). Find other examples. How does this affect the reading of the story? What do you think of it?**

c) One of the main points of the story is that facts get distorted by newspapers and television, and by rumours and 'legends'. Can you think of any examples of this?

About the Author

Jean Rhys was born in Dominica in 1894, just eight years before the eruption of Mt. Pelée, but moved to England when she was sixteen. After an unhappy marriage, she published her first collection of stories in 1927.

Her early books were not very successful, probably because she was too 'modern'; they dealt with the way women were exploited.

In 1939 Jean Rhys disappeared. In fact, people thought she had died. But she reappeared twenty years later, and published some of the stories written while she was 'away'. Then in 1966 her most famous novel, *Wide Sargasso Sea*, was published. It too is set in the Caribbean, and is written as a sort of prelude to Charlotte Bronte's *Jane Eyre*. Jean Rhys died in 1979.

4 A Shadow

by R. K. Narayan

Exercise 1

a) Look at this questionnaire and think about your answers. Don't write them down.

b) Ask another student questions so that you can complete this questionnaire for him or her.

Number of visits to the cinema each year: _____
Number of films made for the cinema seen on T.V. in the last four weeks: _____
Preferences – indicate by putting a number from 1 to 4 beside some of these types of films (1 = favourite):

romantic _____   cartoon _____
crime/murder thriller _____   science fiction _____
war film _____   other: what kind? _____
western _____

Favourite actors:

female _____
male   _____

Favourite film: _____

Exercise 2

Use the following words and others to describe the interior of a cinema and explain where you like to sit when you go to the cinema.

screen   seats   projection room   gangway   lights   exits

Ⓚ **Exercise 3**

All the following words can be used to talk about the feelings that someone might have during or after a film (or a book, T.V. programme etc.).

enjoy   terrify   bored   depress   sadness   fascinating
amusing   anger   horrified   enthusiasm   relieved   joy
absorbing unbearable   surprise   excited   delighted interesting

Put the words in the correct columns in the table at the top of the next page and complete the other columns if possible.

Adjective to describe a film, book etc.	Adjective to describe a person's feelings	Verb	Noun
enjoyable terrifying	—————— terrified	to enjoy to terrify	enjoyment terror

Now use these and other words you know to describe a film you saw recently.

Exercise 4 Look at the two photographs. With a partner invent a story in which they are related.

This story is set in the Tamil area of South India, where the cinema is a very popular form of entertainment. Films for the cinema were originally known as 'moving pictures'. In American English they are called 'movies', and until recently they were often called 'pictures', as in this story.

A Shadow

Sambu demanded, 'You must give me four annas to see the film tomorrow.' His mother was horrified. How could this boy! She had been dreading for six months past the arrival of the film. How could people bear to see him on the screen when they knew he was no
5   more? She had had a vague hope that the producers might not

release the picture out of consideration for her feelings. And when a procession appeared in the street with tom-tom and band, and with young boys carrying placards and huge coloured portraits of her husband, she resolved to go out of town for a while; but it was a desperate and unpractical resolve. Now the picture had arrived. Her husband was going to speak, move and sing, for at least six hours a day in that theatre three streets off.

Sambu was as delighted as if his father had come back to life.

'Mother, won't you also come and see the picture?'

'No.'

'Please, please. You must come.'

She had to explain to him how utterly impossible it would be for her to see the picture. The boy had a sort of ruthless logic: 'Why should it be impossible? Aren't you seeing his photos, even that big photo on the wall, every day?'

'But these photos do not talk, move or sing.'

'And yet you prefer them to the picture which has life!'

The whole of the next day Sambu was in great excitement. In his classroom whenever his master took his eyes off him for a moment he leant over and whispered to his neighbour, 'My father was paid ten thousand rupees to act in that film. I am seeing it this evening. Aren't you also coming?'

'To see *Kumari*!' sneered his friend. He hated Tamil pictures. 'I won't even pass that way.'

'This is not like other Tamil films. My father used to read the story to us every night. It is a very interesting story. He wrote the whole story himself. He was paid ten thousand rupees for writing and acting. I will take you to the picture if you are also coming.'

'I won't see a Tamil picture.'

'This is not an ordinary Tamil picture. It is as good as an English picture.'

But Sambu's friend was adamant. Sambu had to go alone and see the picture. It was an attempt at a new style in Tamil films – a modern story with a minimum of music. It was the story of Kumari, a young girl who refused to marry at fourteen but wanted to study in a university and earn an independent living, and was cast away by her stern father (Sambu's father) and forgiven in the end.

Sambu, sitting in the four-anna class, was eagerly waiting for the picture to begin. It was six months since he had seen his father, and he missed him badly at home.

The hall darkened. Sambu sat through the trailers and slide advertisements without enthusiasm. Finally, his father came on the screen. He was wearing just the dhoti and shirt he used to wear at home; he was sitting at his table just as he used to sit at home. And then a little girl came up, and he patted her on the head and spoke to her exactly as he used to speak to Sambu. And then Father taught the girl arithmetic. She had a slate on her knee and he dictated to her: 'A cartman wants two annas per mile. Rama has three annas on hand. How far will the cartman carry him?' The girl chewed her slate pencil and blinked. Father was showing signs of impatience. 'Go on, Kumari,' Sambu muttered. 'Say something,

tom-tom (*l.7*): a drum played with the hands

placards (*l.8*): posters that can be carried in the street (the cinema owners used these to advertise the new film)

Tamil (*l.28*): one of the most widely used languages in South India

stern (*l.42*): strict, demanding obedience

trailers (*l.46*): advertisements for future films

dhoti (*l.48*): a piece of clothing often worn instead of trousers in India

slate (*l.52*): a thin piece of flat stone previously used for writing on in schools to save paper

cartman (*l.53*): a man whose job is to pull a cart to carry passengers

blinked (*l.55*): shut and opened her eyes quickly

otherwise you will receive a slap presently. I know him better than you do.' Kumari, however, was a better arithmetician than Sambu. She gave the right answer. Father was delighted. How he would
60 jump about in sheer delight whenever Sambu solved a sum correctly! Sambu was reminded of a particular occasion when by sheer fluke he blundered through a puzzle about a cistern with a leak and a tap above it. How Father jumped out of his chair when he heard Sambu declare that it would take three hours for the cistern to fill
65 again.

When the film ended and the lights were switched on, Sambu turned about and gazed at the aperture in the projection room as if his father had vanished into it. The world now seemed to be a poorer place without Father. He ran home. His mother was waiting
70 for him at the door. 'It is nine o'clock. You are very late.'

'I would have loved it if the picture had lasted even longer. You are perverse, Mother. Why won't you see it?'

Throughout the dinner he kept talking. 'Exactly as Father used to sing, exactly as he used to walk, exactly...' His mother listened to
75 him in grim silence.

'Why don't you say something, Mother?'

'I have nothing to say.'

'Don't you like the picture?'

She didn't answer the question. She asked,' Would you like to go
80 and see the picture again tomorrow?'

'Yes, Mother. If possible every day as long as the picture is shown. Will you give me four annas every day?'

'Yes.'

'Will you let me see both the shows every day?'

85 'Oh, no. You can't do that. What is to happen to your lessons?'

'Won't you come and see the picture, Mother?'

'No, impossible.'

For a week more, three hours in the day, Sambu lived in his father's company, and felt depressed at the end of every show.
90 Every day it was a parting for him. He longed to see the night show too, but Mother bothered too much about school lessons. Time was precious, but Mother did not seem to understand it; lessons could wait, but not Father. He envied those who were seeing the picture at night.

95 Unable to withstand his persuasions any more, his mother agreed to see the picture on the last day. They went to the night show. She sat in the women's class. She had to muster all her courage to sit down for the picture. She had a feeling of great relief as long as the slide advertisements and trailer pieces lasted. When the picture
100 began, her heart beat fast. Her husband talking to his wife on the screen, playing with his child, singing, walking, dressing; same clothes, same voice, same anger, same joy – she felt that the whole thing was a piece of cruelty inflicted on her. She shut her eyes several times, but the picture fascinated her: it had the fascination
105 of a thing which is painful. And then came a scene in which he reclined in a chair reading a newspaper. How he would sit absorbed in a newspaper! In their years of married life, how often had she

sheer fluke (*l.61*): pure luck (Sambu didn't use mathematics to solve the problem; he just guessed)

cistern (*l.62*): large water tank

aperture (*l.67*): small opening (through which the film was projected)

perverse (*l.72*): against reason and common sense (a formal word in British English)

muster (*l.97*): gather together

37

quarrelled with him for it! Even on the last day he had sat thus after dinner, in his canvas chair, with the newspaper before him; she had lost her temper at the sight of it and said, 'You and your newspaper! I could as well go and sleep off the rest of the day,' and left his company. When she saw him later, head fallen back in his chair with the sheets of newspaper over his face . . .

110

This was an unbearable scene. A sob burst from her.

115

Sambu, sitting in his seat on the men's side, liked to see his father in the newspaper scene because the girl would presently come and ask him what he was reading, annoy him with questions and get what she deserved: Father would shout, 'Kumari! Will you go out or shall I throw you out?' That girl didn't know how to behave with Father, and Sambu disliked her intensely . . .

120

While awaiting eagerly the snubbing of the girl, Sambu heard a burst of sobbing in the women's class; presently there was a scramble of feet and a cry: 'Put the lights on! Accident to someone!' The show was stopped. People went hither and thither. Sambu, cursing this interruption, stood up on a bench to see what the matter was. He saw his mother being lifted from the floor. 'That's my mother! Is she also dead?' screamed Sambu, and jumped over the barrier. He wailed and cried. Someone told him, 'She has only fainted. Nothing has happened to her. Don't make a fuss.' They carried her out and laid her in the passage. The lights were put out again, people returned to their seats and the show continued. Mother opened her eyes, sat up and said, 'Let us go away.'

125

130

'Yes, Mother.' He fetched a *jutka* and helped her into it. As he was climbing into it himself, from the darkened hall a familiar voice said, 'Kumari! Will you go out or shall I throw you out?' Sambu's heart became heavy and he burst into tears: he was affected both by his mother's breakdown and by the feeling that this was the final parting from his father. They were changing the picture next day.

135

sob (*l.114*): cry of pain or unhappiness
snubbing (*l.121*): unfriendly treatment
jutka (*l.133*): cart pulled by a horse for travelling in

Ⓚ Exercise 5

Answer the following questions.

a) Why did Sambu especially want to see the film 'Kumari'?
b) What was the film about? How was it different from other Tamil films?
c) Why didn't Sambu's mother want to see the film? Why did she decide to go in the end?
d) What happened to her during the film?
e) What were Sambu's feelings when he left the cinema with his mother?

Ⓚ **Exercise 6** Find these phrases in the story, and notice the way in which they are used. In each case circle a), b) or c) to show which you think is the best equivalent. Show which examples are correct in the same way. Of these, usually at least two are correct.

1 'had been dreading' (*line 2*)
   a) had been hoping for
   b) had been thinking about
   c) had been waiting with fear for

2 Which of these are correct:
   a) We are dreading the examination.
   b) The exam dreads the students.
   c) The idea filled them with dread.

3 'he was no more' (*line 4*)
   a) her husband was dead
   b) her husband had no more money
   c) her husband had left film acting

4 'might not release' (*line 5*)
   a) might stop the film being shown
   b) might not send the film there
   c) might not make the film

5 'unpractical resolve' (*line 10*)
   a) a bad solution
   b) a difficult thing to decide
   c) a decision she couldn't carry out

6 'utterly' (*line 17*)
   a) very difficult
   b) absolutely, completely
   c) quite

7 Which of these are correct:
   a) The weather is utterly sunny.
   b) The idea is utterly stupid.
   c) The snow caused utter chaos.

8 'ruthless logic' (*line 18*)
   a) a logical but cruel way of thinking
   b) a clear mind
   c) ideas without much logic

9 'was adamant' (*line 37*)
   a) behaved very cruelly
   b) would not change his mind
   c) was stupid

10 'will receive a slap presently'
(*line 57*)

  a) will soon be hit as a punishment
  b) will often be scolded or told off
  c) will get an interesting present

11 'annoy him with questions'
(*line 117*)

  a) ask him difficult questions
  b) make him angry by asking questions
  c) ask him too many silly questions

12 'cursing this interruption'
(*line 124*)

  a) trying to see what had happened
  b) feeling angry about the interruption
  c) not noticing the interruption

Ⓚ **Exercise 7**

Read the story again and mark the following with F (= it happened in the film), R (= it happened in reality) or B (= it happened both in the film and in reality).

a) The father tried to teach his child arithmetic.   _____
b) The child did a problem about a tank of water.   _____
c) The child did a problem about a cartman.   _____
d) The father jumped out of his chair in surprise.   _____
e) The father sat reading the newspaper.   _____
f) The wife got angry with her husband for reading the paper.   _____
g) The father threatened to throw his child out of the room.   _____
h) The father died while reading the newspaper.   _____

Ⓚ **Exercise 8**

Discuss the story with somebody else and complete the following together.

a) Sambu's school friend did not want to see the film because _____.
b) Sambu's father received 10,000 rupees for _____.
c) For six months Sambu _____, so he felt _____.
d) Sambu's arithmetic was _____ the girl's.
e) Sambu's mother didn't let him go to the cinema more than once a day because _____.
f) On the last day Sambu couldn't sit next to his mother because _____.
g) When he saw people carrying his mother out of the cinema, Sambu thought _____.
h) Sambu cried because _____.

Exercise 9

Group the following words taken from the story under the headings below.

demand   dread   bear   whisper   hope   delighted
explain   depressed   eagerly   mutter   sneer   relief
quarrel   longed   declare   joy   missed

Related to ways of speaking			Related to ways of feeling	
quiet	normal	angry	good/happy	bad/unhappy

Exercise 10

Write a letter from Sambu's mother to her husband's sister in Bombay (who doesn't speak Tamil). Begin like this.

> 67 Madurai Road
> Madras
>
> 23 June
>
> Dear Indira,
>   You may be surprised to receive another letter from me so soon. Please forgive me for troubling you. I feel so upset, so lost, that I have to write to someone, and I naturally thought of you.
>   As I think I told you, Sambu has been going to see *Kumari* every day for the last week. Well, yesterday he finally persuaded . . .

Exercise 11

Discuss these questions with your partner.
- Why does the story have the title 'A Shadow'?
- Who do you feel more sorry for in the end, Sambu or his mother?
- Do you like the story? Why? Why not?

About the Author

R. K. Narayan was born in Madras in Southern India in 1906. He worked for a while in a village school in India after finishing his education, and his first novel, written in 1935, *Swami and Friends*, was about the adventures of a group of schoolboys. He soon gave up teaching to spend all his time on writing. Many of his novels are set in the large, imaginary city of Malgudi in Southern India. They deal with the serious and funny side of everyday life and human relationships in India.

5 I Spy

by Graham Greene

Exercise 1

As they grow up children change a lot both physically and mentally. Can you remember your childhood? What were your character and feelings like at the ages below? In the table, put two ticks (✔✔) to indicate 'very _____', one tick (✔) to indicate 'quite _____' and a cross (✘) to indicate 'not very _____':

	Eight years	Twelve years	Now
confident anxious cheerful daring honest bad tempered talkative other_____ other_____			

Now compare your answers with a partner's. What differences are there?

Exercise 2

Look at this list of adjectives.

impatient   frightened   upset   surprised   shocked
panic-stricken   angry   guilty   pleased   sad

Which of them would apply to you in the following situations, and what would you do? Can you think of other words to describe how you might feel?

- You are alone in a dark place about to steal something. Suddenly you hear a noise near you...
- You are alone in a room. Suddenly people come in, and you hide. While you are hiding you hear a conversation that is private and secret...
- You find out that someone you love has been arrested and taken away by the police...

Exercise 3 Look at the photographs. With a partner invent a story in which they are related.

This story takes place in England late in the First World War (1914–1918). Charlie Stowe is the son of a shopkeeper and lives with his parents above the shop. 'To spy' means to look at something secret (for example a military installation, a secret piece of equipment), or to watch some secret activity in order to give the information to an enemy. A 'spy' is a person who does this. If spies are caught, they are put in prison, and in wartime they may be executed.

I Spy

Charlie Stowe waited until he heard his mother snore before he got out of bed. Even then he moved with caution and tiptoed to the window. The front of the house was irregular, so that it was possible to see a light burning in his mother's room. But now all the windows
5   were dark. A searchlight passed across the sky, lighting the banks of cloud and probing the dark deep spaces between, seeking enemy airships. The wind blew from the sea, and Charlie Stowe could hear behind his mother's snores the beating of the waves. A draught through the cracks in the window-frame stirred his night-shirt.
10 Charlie Stowe was frightened.

But the thought of the tobacconist's shop which his father kept down a dozen wooden stairs drew him on. He was twelve years old, and already boys at the County School mocked him because he had never smoked a cigarette. The packets were piled twelve deep

15 below, Gold Flake and Player's, De Reszke, Abdulla, Woodbines,
and the little shop lay under a thin haze of stale smoke which would
completely disguise his crime. That it was a crime to steal some of
his father's stock Charlie Stowe had no doubt, but he did not love
his father; his father was unreal to him, a wraith, pale, thin,
20 indefinite, who noticed him only spasmodically and left even punishment to his mother. For his mother he felt a passionate demonstra-
tive love; her large boisterous presence and her noisy charity filled
the world for him; from her speech he judged her the friend of
everyone, from the rector's wife to the 'dear Queen', except the
25 'Huns', the monsters who lurked in Zeppelins in the clouds. But his
father's affection and dislike were as indefinite as his movements.
Tonight he had said he would be in Norwich, and yet you never
knew. Charlie Stowe had no sense of safety as he crept down the
wooden stairs. When they creaked he clenched his fingers on the
30 collar of his night-shirt.

At the bottom of the stairs he came out quite suddenly into the
little shop. It was too dark to see his way, and he did not dare touch
the switch. For half a minute he sat in despair on the bottom step
with his chin cupped in his hands. Then the regular movement of
35 the searchlight was reflected through an upper window and the boy
had time to fix in memory the pile of cigarettes, the counter, and the
small hole under it. The footsteps of a policeman on the pavement
made him grab the first packet to his hand and dive for the hole. A
light shone along the floor and a hand tried the door, then the
40 footsteps passed on, and Charlie cowered in the darkness.

At last he got his courage back by telling himself in his curiously
adult way that if he were caught now there was nothing to be done
about it, and he might as well have his smoke. He put a cigarette in
his mouth and then remembered that he had no matches. For a
45 while he dared not move. Three times the searchlight lit the shop, as
he muttered taunts and encouragements. 'May as well be hung for a
sheep,' 'Cowardy, cowardy custard,' grown-up and childish exhor-
tations oddly mixed.

But as he moved he heard footfalls in the street, the sound of
50 several men walking rapidly. Charlie Stowe was old enough to feel
surprise that anybody was about. The footsteps came nearer,
stopped; a key was turned in the shop door, a voice said: 'Let him
in,' and then he heard his father, 'If you wouldn't mind being quiet,
gentlemen. I don't want to wake up the family.' There was a note
55 unfamiliar to Charlie in the undecided voice. A torch flashed and
the electric globe burst into blue light. The boy held his breath; he
wondered whether his father would hear his heart beating, and he
clutched his night-shirt tightly and prayed, 'O God, don't let me be
caught.' Through a crack in the counter he could see his father
60 where he stood, one hand held to his high stiff collar, between two
men in bowler hats and belted mackintoshes. They were strangers.

'Have a cigarette,' his father said in a voice dry as a biscuit. One
of the men shook his head. 'It wouldn't do, not when we are on
duty. Thank you all the same.' He spoke gently, but without
65 kindness: Charlie Stowe thought his father must be ill.

'Mind if I put a few in my pocket?' Mr Stowe asked, and when the man nodded he lifted a pile of Gold Flake and Players from a shelf and caressed the packets with the tips of his fingers.

'Well,' he said, 'there's nothing to be done about it, and I may as 70 well have my smokes.' For a moment Charlie Stowe feared discovery, his father stared round the shop so thoroughly; he might have been seeing it for the first time. 'It's a good little business,' he said, 'for those that like it. The wife will sell out, I suppose. Else the neighbours'll be wrecking it. Well, you want to be off. A stitch in 75 time. I'll get my coat.'

'One of us'll come with you, if you don't mind,' said the stranger gently.

'You needn't trouble. It's on the peg here. There, I'm all ready.'

The other man said in an embarrassed way, 'Don't you want to 80 speak to your wife?' The thin voice was decided. 'Not me. Never do today what you can put off till tomorrow. She'll have her chance later, won't she?'

'Yes, yes,' one of the strangers said and he became very cheerful and encouraging. 'Don't you worry too much. While there's life . . .' 85 and suddenly his father tried to laugh.

When the door had closed Charlie Stowe tiptoed upstairs and got into bed. He wondered why his father had left the house again so late at night and who the strangers were. Surprise and awe kept him for a little while awake. It was as if a familiar photograph had 90 stepped from the frame to reproach him with neglect. He remembered how his father had held tight to his collar and fortified himself with proverbs, and he thought for the first time that, while his mother was boisterous and kindly, his father was very like himself, doing things in the dark which frightened him. It would have 95 pleased him to go down to his father and tell him that he loved him, but he could hear through the window the quick steps going away. He was alone in the house with his mother, and he fell asleep.

caressed (l.68): touched affectionately
Else the neighbours . . . (l.73): 'If she doesn't sell the shop, people in the neighbourhood will ruin it when they know what I've done.'
A stitch in time . . . (l.74): a proverb (see Ex.7)
While there's life . . . (l.84): a proverb (see Ex.7)
awe (l.88): wonder, amazement
fortified himself with (l.92): comforted himself with

Ⓚ **Exercise 4**   **Read the story to find out if the following are *true* or *false*. If there isn't enough information in the story, write *don't know*.**

a) The only noise Charlie could hear was his mother snoring.
b) The house where Charlie lived was near the sea.
c) Charlie's father sold only cigarettes and tobacco in his shop.
d) Charlie felt a lot closer to his mother than to his father.
e) Charlie's father had been to Norwich that day.
f) As he didn't dare to switch on the light, Charlie couldn't see anything in the shop.
g) Charlie had just lit a cigarette when his father came in with two men.
h) Charlie's father didn't expect to return to the shop.
i) Charlie felt closer to his father at the end of the story than at the beginning.

Exercise 5 Find these phrases in the story, and notice the way in which they are used. In each case circle a), b) or c) to show which you think is the best equivalent. Show which examples are correct in the same way. Of these, usually at least two are correct.

1 'tiptoed to the window' (*line 2*)
   a) walked on his hands and knees
   b) walked with very big steps
   c) walked very quietly, on his toes

2 '. . . was irregular' (*line 3*)
   a) not flat or in line
   b) badly built
   c) built of rough stone

3 'A searchlight passed . . .' (*line 5*)
   a) there was an electric storm
   b) a big light was being used to look for enemy activity in the sky
   c) planes with lights were flying in the area

4 'enemy airships' (*line 6*)

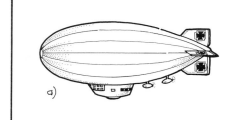  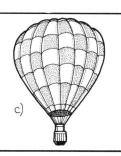

5 'A draught . . . stirred . . .' (*line 8*)
   a) his night shirt moved in the current of air
   b) the window was open and he felt cold
   c) he was so frightened that he was trembling

6 'mocked him . . .' (*line 13*)
   a) laughed at him
   b) were very surprised
   c) thought he was stupid

7 Which of these are correct:
   a) Are you mocking my new hairstyle?
   b) The film makes me mock.
   c) Don't mock those who are unhappy.

8 'thin haze of stale smoke' (*line 16*)
   a) a strong smell of old tobacco smoke
   b) an unpleasant cloud of tobacco smoke
   c) a light mist of tobacco smoke

9 Which of these are correct:
   a) There was haze coming from the boiling water.
   b) I only have a hazy memory of my childhood.
   c) The morning haze lay over the valley.

10 'his father's stock' (*line 18*)
   a) his father's belongings
   b) the goods in his father's shop
   c) his father's favourite things

11 'noisy charity' (*line 22*)
   a) her loud laughter
   b) her cheerful kindness
   c) her love of life in general

12 Which of these are correct:
   a) The old lady gave her money to charity.
   b) That wasn't a charitable thing to say.
   c) He gave the old beggar a charity.

13 'monsters who lurked...' (*line 25*)
   a) airships like strange, imaginary animals
   b) clouds looking like ugly creatures
   c) the cruel enemy soldiers waiting silently in the airships

14 'clenched his fingers...' (*line 29*)
   a) he held his collar tightly, in fear
   b) his fingers trembled as he held the collar
   c) he had to hold his collar together to keep warm

15 'dive for the hole' (*line 38*)
   a) go head-first into the hole
   b) move very quickly in order to hide
   c) put his head down

16 'muttered taunts...' (*line 46*) a) talked to himself in order to feel braver

b) sang a song very quietly

c) spoke in an angry way, as if to a friend

17 Which of these are correct: a) 'I'm hungry,' he muttered.

b) He muttered me during the film.

c) Stop muttering. I can't hear you.

Ⓚ **Exercise 6** **The following words from the story all relate to the lights or the sounds which are important to the atmosphere of the story. Group them in the two boxes below.**

probed   shone   creaked   pale   note   reflected
burst   beating   snore   burn   dry   muttered   haze
flashed

Light	Sound

Ⓚ **Exercise 7** **Proverbs and sayings play an important part in this story. Most of them are incomplete. Match the beginnings of these proverbs (some from the story and some not) with the correct endings.**

1 A stitch in time...   a) ...what you can do today

2 You may as well be hung for a sheep...   b) ...there's hope

3 Never put off till tomorrow ...   c) ...has a silver lining

4 People who live in glasshouses ...   d) ...in the mouth

5 While there's life...   e) ...as for a lamb

6 Don't look a gift-horse...   f) ...saves nine

7 Every cloud...   g) ...shouldn't throw stones

Now match the complete proverbs with the correct meanings.

- don't give up until you're dead
- if somebody offers you something free, don't criticise it
- even unhappy events may have their good side
- do things immediately if you can – don't delay
- if you do something at the right time you can save yourself a lot of trouble later

- if you are going to get caught for a crime, it may as well be a big crime
- don't criticise other people if you are in danger of being criticised yourself

Exercise 8

Discuss the following with a partner.

a) Imagine you are Charlie. It is the next morning. Your mother thinks your father is in Norwich and will return later in the day. You know it isn't true. You can't bear to keep your secret any longer. What do you say to your mother? How much of the truth do you tell her?

b) Who do you feel most sorry for at the end of the story; Charlie, his father or his mother?

c) What is the real 'message' of the story?

Exercise 9

Imagine that Charlie Stowe kept a diary in which he wrote down his private thoughts and feelings. Write an entry for the morning after his father's arrest. Begin like this.

Tuesday 16th March

I woke up thinking that I had had a nightmare. But it wasn't a dream: it really happened. I saw it with my own eyes...

Ⓚ Exercise 10

In *line 28*, Greene writes: 'Charlie Stowe had no sense of safety as he crept down the wooden stairs. When they creaked, he clenched his fingers...'. **Find four other phrases in the story which show how frightened Charlie was. Do you find the phrases effective in describing his fear? If so, why?**

About the Author

Graham Greene was born in England in 1904. After leaving Oxford University he worked as a journalist on *The Times*. Later he travelled widely, and he has written several novels set in other countries, including *The Power and the Glory* (Mexico), *The Heart of the Matter* (West Africa), *The Quiet American* (Vietnam), and *The Comedians* (Haiti). Greene has written about thirty novels and a number of children's books and travel books, as well as short stories. Many of Greene's novels have been made into films.

6 Dead Men's Path

by Chinua Achebe

Exercise 1   **Answer the following questions about your superstitions and beliefs.**
1 Is the number 13 unlucky for you? ———— Do you have a lucky number? What is it? ————
2 What do you do if you drop salt on the table? ————
3 What do you feel if you see a black cat run across the street? ————
4 Do you believe in ghosts? ———— Have you ever seen one? ————
5 What other superstitions do you have? ————

Now compare your superstitions and beliefs with two partners.

Exercise 2   **Changes take place in all countries, and in every town and village. List some of the changes which have happened over the past 50 years in the place where your home is.**

Good changes	Bad changes

Ⓚ Exercise 3   **Some of the following words from the story usually have a positive meaning and some usually have a negative meaning.**
a) Group the words under Positive or Negative.
b) If you can, find opposites of the words and put them on the same line. Use a dictionary if necessary.

unprogressive   energetic   responsible   enthusiastic
delightful   backward   nasty   wonderful   sceptical
fantastic   admirable

Positive	Negative

Exercise 4

Look at the two pictures carefully. With a partner, invent a story in which the two could be connected.

This story is set in Nigeria in West Africa at a time when the country was changing very fast. As in many countries, some places, such as the larger cities, were changing more quickly than others, and some people, especially the younger ones, wanted things to change dramatically, while others wanted things to stay as they were.

Dead Men's Path

Michael Obi's hopes were fulfilled much earlier than he had expected. He was appointed headmaster of Ndume Central School in January 1949. It had always been an unprogressive school, so the Mission authorities decided to send a young and energetic man to
5   run it. Obi accepted this responsibility with enthusiasm. He had many wonderful ideas and this was an opportunity to put them into practice. He had had sound secondary school education which designated him a 'pivotal teacher' in the official records and set him apart from the other headmasters in the mission field. He was
10   outspoken in his condemnation of the narrow views of these older and often less-educated ones.

'We shall make a good job of it, shan't we?' he asked his young wife when they first heard the joyful news of his promotion.

'We shall do our best,' she replied. 'We shall have such beautiful
15   gardens and everything will be just *modern* and delightful...' In their two years of married life she had become completely infected by his passion for 'modern methods' and his denigration of 'these

Glossary

Mission (*l.4*): in Africa many schools were started and managed by religious missions aiming to spread Christianity
designated (*l.8*): classified him officially
pivotal (*l.8*): very important
denigration (*l.17*): strong criticism

51

old and superannuated people in the teaching field who would be better employed as traders in the Onitsha market'. She began to see
20 herself already as the admired wife of the young headmaster, the queen of the school.

The wives of the other teachers would envy her position. She would set the fashion in everything... Then, suddenly, it occurred to her that there might not be other wives. Wavering between hope
25 and fear, she asked her husband, looking anxiously at him.

'All our colleagues are young and unmarried,' he said with enthusiasm which for once she did not share. 'Which is a good thing,' he continued.

'Why?'

30 'Why? They will give all their time and energy to the school.'

Nancy was downcast. For a few minutes she became sceptical about the new school; but it was only for a few minutes. Her little personal misfortune could not blind her to her husband's happy prospects. She looked at him as he sat folded up in a chair. He was
35 stoop-shouldered and looked frail. But he sometimes surprised people with sudden bursts of physical energy. In his present posture, however, all his bodily strength seemed to have retired behind his deep-set eyes, giving them an extraordinary power of penetration. He was only twenty-six, but looked thirty or more. On the whole,
40 he was not unhandsome.

'A penny for your thoughts, Mike,' said Nancy after a while, imitating the woman's magazine she read.

'I was thinking what a grand opportunity we've got at last to show these people how a school should be run.' Ndume School was
45 backward in every sense of the word. Mr Obi put his whole life into the work, and his wife hers too. He had two aims. A high standard of teaching was insisted upon, and the school compound was to be turned into a place of beauty. Nancy's dream-gardens came to life with the coming of the rains, and blossomed. Beautiful hibiscus and
50 allamanda hedges in brilliant red and yellow marked out the carefully tended school compound from the rank neighbourhood bushes.

One evening as Obi was admiring his work he was scandalized to see an old woman from the village hobble right across the compound, through a marigold flower-bed and the hedges. On going up
55 there he found faint signs of an almost disused path from the village across the school compound to the bush on the other side.

'It amazes me,' said Obi to one of his teachers who had been three years in the school, 'that you people allowed the villagers to make use of this footpath. It is simply incredible.' He shook his
60 head.

'The path,' said the teacher apologetically, 'appears to be very important to them. Although it is hardly used, it connects the village shrine with their place of burial.'

'And what has that got to do with the school?' asked the head-
65 master.

'Well, I don't know,' replied the other with a shrug of the shoulders. 'But I remember there was a big row some time ago when we attempted to close it.'

superannuated (l.18): people with out-of-date ideas who should retire
stoop-shouldered (l.35): with a rounded back
frail (l.35): weak
blossomed (l.49): flowered
hibiscus and allamanda (l.49): flowering bushes
tended (l.51): looked after
rank (l.51): growing in an uncontrolled way
hobble (l.53): walk as if in pain
marigold (l.54): a bright orange flower
shrine (l.63): religious place

52

'That was some time ago. But it will not be used now,' said Obi as he walked away. 'What will the Government Education Officer think of this when he comes to inspect the school next week? The villagers might, for all I know, decide to use the schoolroom for a pagan ritual during the inspection.'

Heavy sticks were planted closely across the path at the two places where it entered and left the school premises. These were further strengthened with barbed wire.

Three days later the village priest of *Ani* called on the headmaster. He was an old man and walked with a slight stoop. He carried a stout walking-stick which he usually tapped on the floor, by way of emphasis, each time he made a new point in his argument.

'I have heard,' he said after the usual exchange of cordialities, 'that our ancestral footpath has recently been closed...'

'Yes,' replied Mr Obi. 'We cannot allow people to make a highway of our school compound.'

'Look here, my son,' said the priest bringing down his walking-stick, 'this path was here before you were born and before your father was born. The whole life of this village depends on it. Our dead relatives depart by it and our ancestors visit us by it. But most important, it is the path of children coming in to be born...'

Mr Obi listened with a satisfied smile on his face.

'The whole purpose of our school,' he said finally, 'is to eradicate just such beliefs as that. Dead men do not require footpaths. The whole idea is just fantastic. Our duty is to teach your children to laugh at such ideas.'

'What you say may be true,' replied the priest, 'but we follow the practices of our fathers. If you re-open the path we shall have nothing to quarrel about. What I always say is: let the hawk perch and let the eagle perch.' He rose to go.

'I am sorry,' said the young headmaster. 'But the school compound cannot be a thoroughfare. It is against our regulations. I would suggest your constructing another path, skirting our premises. We can even get our boys to help in building it. I don't suppose the ancestors will find the little detour too burdensome.'

'I have no more words to say,' said the old priest, already outside.

Two days later a young woman in the village died in childbed. A diviner was immediately consulted and he prescribed heavy sacrifices to propitiate ancestors insulted by the fence.

Obi woke up next morning among the ruins of his work. The beautiful hedges were torn up not just near the path but right round the school, the flowers trampled to death and one of the school buildings pulled down... That day, the white Supervisor came to inspect the school and wrote a nasty report on the state of the premises but more seriously about the 'tribal-war situation developing between the school and the village, arising in part from the misguided zeal of the new headmaster'.

pagan ritual (l.73): a religious ceremony which is not Christian

cordialities (l.82): politeness

let the hawk... (l.98): let people with different beliefs do different things; live and let live

thoroughfare (l.101): a public path

burdensome (l.104): difficult, annoying

diviner (l.107): someone who has the power to explain the causes of certain things

propitiate (l.108): win the pardon or forgiveness of someone

misguided zeal (l.116): unwise enthusiasm

ⓚ Exercise 5   Answer the following questions about the story.

1 Was Michael Obi expecting to become a head teacher at the age of 26?
2 What was Nancy Obi's main interest in the new school?
3 Why was Michael Obi so shocked to see an old woman walking across the compound?
4 How did Mr Obi try to stop people using the path?
5 Why did the priest come to the school?
6 What did the villagers do to the new gardens?

ⓚ Exercise 6   Look at the story again in order to complete the following information briefly.

Example
1 Michael Obi's reason for being pleased with his new post: <u>It was a chance to carry out some of his progressive ideas.</u>
2 Nancy Obi's reason for looking forward to the posting: _____
3 Michael Obi's appearance and age: _____
4 Changes made by the Obis at Ndume School:
   a) _____
   b) _____
   c) _____
5 The importance of the path to the villagers: _____
6 Differences between the attitudes of:
   a) Mr Obi _____
   b) the village priest _____
7 Reasons for the damage to the school compound: _____
8 The inspector's impression of the school: _____

ⓚ Exercise 7   Find these phrases in the story, and notice the way in which they are used. In each case circle a), b) or c) to show which you think is the best equivalent. Show which examples are correct in the same way. Of these, usually at least two are correct.

1 'sound . . . education' (*line 7*)
   a) part of his education
   b) a good secondary education
   c) a long secondary education

2 Which of these are correct:
   a) The politician has some sound ideas.
   b) His voice sounded strange.
   c) Don't make so much sound.

3 'outspoken in his condemnation' (*line 10*)
   a) he spoke very loudly
   b) he spoke for a long time about his ideas
   c) he wasn't afraid of speaking critically

4 'infected by his passion' (*line 16*)

    a) influenced by his ideas
    b) deeply in love with him
    c) sick of his opinions

5 'Wavering between hope and fear' (*line 24*)

    a) sometimes she was hopeful, and sometimes she was afraid
    b) she was trapped between good and bad feelings
    c) wondering what was going to happen

6 'downcast' (*line 31*)

    a) thoughtful
    b) very surprised
    c) unhappy

7 'A penny for your thoughts' (*line 41*)

    a) tell me what you're thinking
    b) you have some good ideas
    c) you're being silly

8 'scandalized' (*line 52*)

    a) amused
    b) surprised
    c) horrified

9 'big row' (*line 67*)

    a) a long procession
    b) a big disagreement
    c) a lot of noise

10 'eradicate just such beliefs' (*line 92*)

    a) increase people's religious feeling
    b) make people change their ideas
    c) get rid of that kind of belief

11 'skirting our premises' (*line 102*)

    a) going round the edge of the school compound
    b) in a different part of the village
    c) through a different part of the compound

Exercise 8

Imagine you are the inspector who visited the school, the author of the 'nasty report' to be sent to the Ministry. Begin it like this.

Report on a visit to Ndume Central School

The school is situated in the middle of a pleasant country village. It has about 250 pupils, and seven teachers. The headmaster, Mr Obi, was only appointed six months ago. I am afraid to say that his first year is not going well...

Exercise 9

Discuss the following.

a) Who was in the wrong in this story: Mr Obi or the villagers? Why?

b) Which of the following should schools today try to do:
  - get rid of superstitious beliefs
  - teach clear religious beliefs and give clear guidance about right and wrong
  - help pupils understand politics so they are ready to vote
  - give sex education
  - give health education so that people live and eat better
  - make sure pupils practise sports and do lots of exercise
  - teach pupils to be 'patriotic'
  - get pupils to think for themselves and not to be ready to believe what they hear at home, on T.V., at school, from politicians etc. without question
  - other (what?) _____

c) 'Let the hawk perch and let the eagle perch' or 'Live and let others live'. Do you agree that we should be tolerant of other people's beliefs and behaviour? What 'rights' should everybody have to choose their own religion, or to choose no religion at all? How should governments and other people in authority take account of the fact that in some places, 'modernisation' is easier than in others, and that some people are more ready to change?

Ⓚ Exercise 10

In *line 43* Mr Obi says: 'I was thinking what a grand opportunity we've got at last to show these people how a school should be run'. **What does this phrase tell us about Mr Obi? List five other phrases which the writer uses to give the reader a clear idea of Mr Obi's character. What effect does this 'portrait' of Mr Obi have on the reader? Would you have done it differently if you had been the writer?**

About the Author

Chinua Achebe was born in Nigeria and educated at University College, Ibadan. From 1954–1966 he worked for the Nigerian Broadcasting Corporation. He became famous as a writer after the publication of his novels *Things Fall Apart* (1958) and *No Longer at Ease* (1960), both of which are published in many countries. These, like his stories, deal with the problems of Africans living in Africa in the twentieth century.

7 A Tree Falls

by Roger Mais

Exercise 1 Most people live in cities or towns. They only visit 'country' areas at weekends or during holidays. Which of the following do you like best and which do you think are most important for the future of your country and the world? Write numbers 1 to 6 in the boxes for each of these geographical features (1 = most important/most beautiful/most fun), and give reasons in each case. Then compare your answers with a partner's.

	Beautiful	Fun to visit	Important
mountains			
deserts			
lakes			
beach/coast			
forest/woods			
rivers			

Exercise 2 Wood is a very important natural resource.

a) **Which of these purposes is it used for in your country?**
- making furniture
- building houses
- fuel for cooking
- fuel for heating
- making paper and cardboard
- making vehicles
- railway lines
- other (what?) _____

b) **Find out where the main forests are in your country and what kinds of trees grow in them.**

c) **Imagine yourself alone in a large forest. Which of the following do you associate with being there?**
- silence
- noise
- darkness
- light
- fear
- excitement
- danger
- peace
- other (what?) _____

Compare your answers with a partner's.

d) These words from the story are related to trees. Use them to label the diagrams below.

roots   trunk   branches (or boughs)   leaves
twig   sapling   underbrush (or undergrowth)

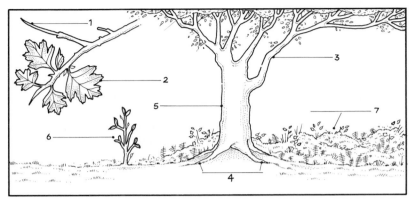

Exercise 3

Look at these two photographs. Alone or with a partner try to think up the outline of a story in which they could be related.

This story takes place in a forest in Jamaica at the time before independence (i.e. before 1962), when Jamaica was still a British colony. The forest belonged to the government (or Crown), and only they could authorise the cutting down of trees. Forest-Rangers (sort of policemen) patrolled the forest to make sure people weren't cutting trees down illegally.

A Tree Falls

He laid aside the axe, and the waves of silence that had parted before him as he made his careless way to the heart of the forest, flowed back as with a sigh. The silence flattened itself out over the entire vast valley, clothing the rocks and the trees, thick and
5 palpable like the river mist – hiding at its patient core the certain knowledge that even the axe with its rude foreign exclamations, venturing there with the brave clamour that cloaks fear, foretold its own stammering, inevitable surrender.

It seemed to him that he heard stealthy footsteps somewhere
10 behind him . . . the snapping of dried twigs . . . the leafy whisper of green ones, as invisible fingers put them aside to allow unhindered the passage of the ghostly inhabitants of the wilderness.

He made no attempt to turn his head, because he knew he would see no one . . . and ever the silence would settle back with the
15 passing of these tiny ripples of sound that ringed its smooth surface . . .

Again the axe sang its victorious note against the thin, vibrating walls that took it and threw it backward and forward, multiplying it a thousand times.
20 Fresh chips from the great tree spattered the coffee-brown of its rotted leaves of centuries . . . It creaks throughout its mighty girth . . . It teeters – or so it seems – with the thrust of the wind through its boughs that have reached during its lifetime ever triumphantly upward, until they tower a hundred feet in the air.
25 It is leaning a little now . . . it yearns over the valley that has known it these hundred years, where it has spread the tallest shadow, and wove the silence within its leaves and branches, like the shuttles of a tremendous loom, spinning away the close fabric of tremendous and unending twilight that might shadow the heart of
30 the stoutest with unreasoning terror.

The man is exultant. The wound in the tree's side has laid bare the great red heart of mahogany. In this tree there is a small fortune for the taking. There is not another tree like it in all the length and breadth of these virgin wooded Crown lands.
35 The men with the saws are in the hills beyond, keeping a watchful lookout for the Crown Forest-Rangers – for the thunder of his axe travels far in this wilderness. If a Ranger should appear they will make the smoke-signal, while ostensibly roasting wild Imba-roots over a fire. They will, if necessary, keep the Ranger there, swapping
40 stories with him, allowing him to fill his pipe from their supply of tobacco, offering him roasted Imba-root and jerked pork on the end of a sharpened stick.

He is alone in the valley with this giant that is slowly bowing to his relentless axe.
45 He is forced to pause again to rest and catch his breath . . . the giant is tougher even than he thought. Stubbornly the great axe stands, resisting valiantly to the last the terrible assaults of the axe.

He is tired . . . he leans heavily against the handle of his axe, the

Glossary

sigh (*l.3*): drawing in of breath because of sadness

palpable (*l.5*): in a way that you could feel

core (*l.5*): centre

venturing there . . . surrender (*l.7*): the silence 'knows' that even the noise of the axe will eventually be 'defeated' by the silence

unhindered (*l.11*): with nothing to stop them

Fresh chips spattered . . . (*l.20*): little pieces of wood spread over the ground

girth (*l.21*): width of the trunk

teeters (*l.22*): rocks as if about to fall

yearns (*l.25*): reaches out as if it wants to move into the valley

shuttles . . . loom (*l.28*): the branches of the tree are compared to a machine for making cloth

stoutest (*l.30*): strongest and bravest person

exultant (*l.31*): full of happiness

mahogany (*l.32*) *cedar* (*l.68*): kinds of tree or wood

swapping (*l.39*): exchanging

jerked pork (*l.41*): pork preserved by drying in the sun

blade of which is buried so deep into the solid heart of the tree, that
50 his full weight upon it will not shake the axe.

Silence fills the valley again. Ghostly whispers of silence ... the
snapping of dried twigs, now here, now there ... the sibilant query
and protest of leaves in the underbrush that part to let the ghostly
ones pass ... then the ripples on the face of silence are smoothed
55 over, as it settles back again, calm and enigmatic like the face of a
pool, or a poker-player.

He is a brave man, not easily frightened. He is inured to the
menace of the wilderness, its silence. Yet strange sensations tingle
down his sweating spine. Strange thoughts thrust aside the one that
60 was uppermost in his mind ... the gloating triumph of the moment.

And then they turned to home and the woman who waited his
coming – herself a tree – a sapling tree heavy with the promise of
fruitage.

There would be a great round pan of corn-pone in the kitchen,
65 cold, when he got back ... and a woman's arms about him – his
woman.

The extension he was adding to their home would need some
hardwood joists and beams, and cedar shingles for the roof. He
would use only the finest native lumber, as usual. The finest native
70 lumber to be had in these parts came from off the vast wooden
tracts of virgin Crown lands. It was his for the taking, if only he
could out-smart the Government Rangers and Bailiffs.

In the out-shed, hidden away under the bundle of shavings, was
the wooden axe he was carving as a gift for the son that would be
75 his. It just had to be a boy, because he didn't have any use for girl
children. What in the world would he do with her? His boy now,
would become a lumber-man like himself, like his father was before
him. He would teach him all the tricks of the trade ... He would be
well equipped to carry on the traditions of the family, and grow up
80 to be a prosperous and respected citizen.

There would be a thick slab of corn-pone in the kitchen on his
return ...

Again the strange thoughts – unnamed fears, premonitions ... the
quick snapping of twigs ... a sudden scurry of fallen leaves along the
85 forest floor ... overhead the giant tree trembled and groaned in its
agony ...

His eyes went suddenly to the crest of the furthest hill.

Was that the signal of his men? He put a hand to his forehead and
peered out from beneath it. No, it was only a wisp of cloud, like a
90 ghostly, nebulous, writhing axe ... an axe imbedded in the heart of
a great tree of cloud. For a moment it seemed to him menacing with
omen.

He laughed at his own fears, and was immediately shocked and
abashed by the profound, pained silence that followed it. Strange
95 that the valley did not echo his laughter. He laughed again – louder
and longer this time – then cupped his hand to his ear, leaning
forward, every nerve strained, listening. From far down the valley

sibilant query (l.52):
  whispering sound like a
  question
inured to (l.57): not affected
  by, completely used to
corn-pone (l.64): bread made
  of maize
joists, beams (l.68): lengths of
  wood to support the roof
shingles (l.68): thin, flat
  pieces of wood to cover a
  roof or wall
lumber (l.69): wood prepared
  for use in building etc.
out-shed (l.73): small wooden
  hut to keep tools in
menacing with omen (l.91):
  threatening some unhappy
  future event

came a thin whisper of derisive echoes.

He put his head back defiantly and opened his mouth to laugh
100 again, distending his bellows-like lungs to their fullest...and suddenly changed his mind.

He knocked with the heel of his hand sharply against the handle
of the axe, several times, to make it loosen its death grip upon the
tree. Then he swung it aloft again.

105 He could hear the ringing, exultant echoes of the axe, though
...the mean silence of the valley dared not withhold that sound!
The triumphant, gloating laughter of the axe split that silence in two
again, throwing it back upon itself in great twin waves that towered
higher than the mountains themselves. Very well then, they would
110 heed the sound of his axe and tremble! His heart filled to bursting
with pride. He added his own rhythmic grunt at the end of each
stroke, to the voice of the axe.

The great tree-trunk that had mocked the strength of his arm, and
the silence that had mocked his puny laughter...they belonged to
115 the stubborn reluctance of the unyielding wilderness, his ancient
antagonist. But he would show them who was conqueror here,
wilderness or man...heart of tree, or blade of axe...

He would show them...*show* them...*show* them...!

Was that the sound of the giant timber yielding, the great heart of
120 wood breaking at last...? or was it just another trick of the
wilderness, trying to fool him again, trying to delay the ultimate
conquest of his strong arm and his sharp axe-blade over insensate
timber? He would show them...*show* them...*show* them! Each
stroke of the axe seemed to bite deeper, deeper. The chips flew in a
125 shower round him...red chips now...chips from the unyielding
red heart of mahogany!...

Without further warning the great tree suddenly bowed, seemed to
hesitate an instant, suspended at an impossible slant, yet reluctant
to the last, battling against the inevitable to the last. Then with a
130 mighty roar it thundered to the ground. The trunk leaped in the air,
gave a spasmodic sideways kick as the tough branches a hundred
feet away, hit the first obstacle of rock. Then it reared high up
again, as though it would complete a somersault, and crashed to its
side, lying with the angle of the valley.

135 A flight of winged reverberations took the air sharply, with a
mighty thrust of wings – for an instant only – then came quietly to
rest again among the branches of the trees and upon the naked
spurs of rock. And the waves of silence flowed forward over the
valley, covering everything, healing the terrible instant of thunder
140 that had gashed it across.

He had heard the last unmistakable crackle of the falling tree. He
had barely time to leap aside, leaving his axe there, sunk in its
heart. He saw the lower end rear up into the air, and his heart was
almost humbled for a moment. He had sent yet another giant
145 thundering to his doom...and almost in the same instant his heart
knew terror as he saw the quick sideways kick of the jagged base,
spurred and weighted with death. He had no time to avoid it...an

bellows (*l.100*): air pump
operated by hand to make a
fire burn
gloating (*l.107*): cruel and
happy
puny (*l.114*): weak
slant (*l.128*): angle
gashed (*l.140*): cut like a
knife

instant of triumph . . . a split instant of panic . . . and then – nothing
. . .

150   Dusk was settling down over the valley when the sawyers came. They saw the place where the mighty tree had fallen. They shouted their joy and quickened their pace, until they came to the spot where *his* broken body lay.

They stood with bared heads, and tight lips, staring at him. The
155   silence . . . the snapping of dried twigs . . . the ghostly whispers of leaves . . . all these daunted them . . .

They left him where he lay within that vast, that weirdly peopled sepulchre of silence.

sawyers (l.150): men who cut up timber with large saws

Ⓚ **Exercise 4**   Read the story quickly to find out if the following are *true* or *false*. If there isn't enough information in the story, write *don't know*.
a) The man was frightened of the forest.
b) It was not easy to cut the tree down.
c) The Forest-Rangers had heard the noise of his axe.
d) He was cutting down the tree to get wood for building.
e) The man had a young son.
f) If the other men saw the Rangers they would run to warn him.
g) It took the man several hours to cut the tree down.
h) The man was killed by his own axe.

Ⓚ **Exercise 5**   Find these phrases in the story, and notice the way in which they are used. In each case circle a), b) or c) to show which you think is the best equivalent. Show which examples are correct in the same way. Of these, usually at least two are correct.

1 'entire vast valley' (*line 4*)   a) the bottom of the valley
                                       b) the whole enormous valley
                                       c) the quiet and huge valley

2 Which of these are correct: a) The entire village was destroyed.
                                  b) The equipment isn't entire; there's something missing.
                                  c) The Sahara Desert is entire.

3 'unending twilight' (*line 29*)   a) the light that never dies
                                       b) a bright light stretching to the horizon
                                       c) dull light like that between day and night continuing for a long time

62

4 'virgin . . . lands' (*line 34*)

    a) unspoilt forests, none of which is cut down

    b) land covered with young, beautiful trees

    c) land with only a few trees on it

5 'while ostensibly roasting' (*line 38*)

    a) while trying to cook the roots

    b) while showing the Ranger how to cook the roots

    c) while pretending to cook the roots

6 'Stubbornly' (*line 46*)

    a) strongly

    b) as if refusing to fall

    c) majestically

7 Which of these are correct:

    a) He wears stubborn clothes.

    b) Do as you're told and don't be stubborn.

    c) She stood stubbornly and refused to move.

8 'enigmatic' (*line 55*)

    a) it is hard to guess its 'feelings'

    b) it seems very dangerous

    c) it is quite serene

9 'heavy . . . fruitage' (*line 62*)

    a) the woman told him there would be fruit for supper

    b) she liked eating fruit so much that she was overweight

    c) she was expecting a baby

10 'peered out' (*line 89*)

    a) felt a headache coming

    b) looked in a very intent way

    c) shaded his eyes from the sun

11 'swung it aloft' (*line 104*)

    a) lifted it high

    b) rested it on his shoulder

    c) balanced it between his hands

12 Which of these are correct:

    a) The clock pendulum was swinging back and forth.

    b) There are swings in the play-ground.

    c) She swung her head in agree-ment.

13 'mocked' (*line 113*)
    a) laughed at
    b) hurt
    c) removed

14 'unyielding' (*line 115*)
    a) not changing in any way
    b) not giving in to his efforts
    c) not making a sound

15 'humbled' (*line 144*)
    a) full of joy and pride
    b) full of relief that the effort was over
    c) made to feel small and, in a way, sorry

16 'daunted' (*line 156*)
    a) made them sad
    b) filled them with fear
    c) made them angry because of his death

Ⓚ **Exercise 6**

a) In the list of words from the story below, some of the words have to do with sound and some with movement. Put the words in the appropriate list.

snapping   vibrating   creak   leaped   bowed   ringing
echo   kick   grunt   reared   roar   somersault
groaned   thundered   crackle   flowed

Sound	Movement

b) Select words from the list above to match these subjects and situations.

- Church bells on a Sunday   _____
- Pigs waiting to be fed   _____
- A heavy door in an old castle   _____
- An acrobat at a circus   _____
- A bad telephone line   _____
- A lion preparing to attack   _____
- Actors at the end of a play   _____
- A jazz musician's fingers   _____
- Somebody not happy with their job   _____
- A horse jumping over a fence   _____

(K) Exercise 7

a) **In *line 15*, the writer makes a connection between silence and a pool of water.**
- how does he do it?
- which other line(s) does he do it in?
- why does he do it?
- do you think this image is a good one in the context of the story?

b) **In *line 43*, the writer makes a connection between the tree and a giant.**
- does he use the image in other parts of the story?
- why does he use it?
- do you think it works well in the context of the story?

c) **What is the main message of the story? What do you think of the way in which the author presents it, and the way in which the story is written?**

Exercise 8

Write two paragraphs continuing the story. You may want to include
- the woman mentioned in the story
- the Forest-Rangers
- the tree
- the sawyers

Exercise 9

Do you agree or disagree with the following.
- Governments should spend much more money on protecting and replanting forests.
- Nature is too strong; man can't really do any damage to the natural environment.
- Air pollution from power stations, factories and vehicles causes acid rain, which kills trees and fish in lakes. But we have to have power and industry and it isn't worth spending millions installing filters.
- All paper for packing, newspapers and magazines should be recycled to save cutting down trees.

About the Author

Roger Mais was born in Jamaica in 1905. After finishing school he became a journalist, and he soon began writing not just for the newspapers but for himself; he had two collections of short stories published at his own expense. Mais soon became involved in politics and in particular in the Jamaican nationalist movement. An article he produced in 1944 criticising the colonialist strategy of the British government under Churchill led to six months in prison. Mais was a national hero. After his release from prison, Mais dedicated his efforts mainly to his writing and to painting. He produced several novels but was frustrated with the limitations he felt in Jamaica. He left for Europe in 1952 to pursue his literary career. But he fell ill and returned to Jamaica. Mais died of cancer in 1955.

8 A High Dive

by L. P. Hartley

Exercise 1   The story is about a circus. Answer these questions.
- Have you ever been to a circus?

If yes:

- When did you last go to one?

  _____
- Did you enjoy it? _____
- Why/Why not? _____

If no:

- Would you like to go?

  _____
- Why/Why not? _____

Exercise 2   Which of the following acts have you seen at the circus, or on T.V.? Put a ✔ or ✖ in the space provided. Then put numbers 1 to 3 beside three very enjoyable acts (1 = most enjoyable). Discuss your choices with a partner.

a) clowns   _____

b) trapeze artists   _____

c) lion/tiger tamer   _____

d) acrobats   _____

e) wall of death   _____

f) tightrope walker   _____

g) human cannonball   _____

h) other (what?)   _____

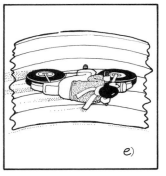

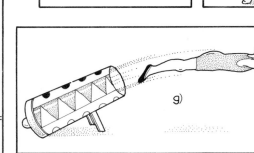

Exercise 3
Look at the two photographs. With a partner, invent a story in which they are related.

ⓚ Exercise 4
a) Pair the following adjectives so that each adjective is with its opposite (or one of its opposites).

Example   common/unusual

common	exciting
dangerous	relaxing
amusing	safe
tiring	boring
unusual	sad

b) Now complete the following about spare-time activities.

1 I think it's relaxing to _____.
2 I enjoy _____ because it's exciting.
3 It isn't very safe to _____.
4 I usually find _____ amusing.
5 In my opinion it's dangerous _____.
6 I find _____ tiring.

This story is set in a circus in England during or just after the Second World War. Like most circuses at the time, this one was owned and managed by one family.

A High Dive

The circus-manager was worried. Attendances had been falling off
and such people as did come – children they were, mostly – sat
about listlessly, munching sweets or sucking ices, sometimes talking
to each other without so much as glancing at the show. Only the
5 young or little girls, who came to see the ponies, betrayed any real
interest. The clowns' jokes fell flat, for they were the kind of jokes
that used to raise a laugh before 1939, after which critical date
people's sense of humour seemed to have changed, along with many
other things about them. The circus-manager had heard the word
10 'corny' flung about and didn't like it. What did they want? Something that was, in his opinion, sillier and more pointless than the old
jokes; not a bull's-eye on the target of humour, but an outer or even
a near-miss – something that brought in the element of futility and
that could be laughed at as well as with: an unintentional joke
15 against the joker. The clowns were quick enough with their patter
but it just didn't go down: there was too much sense in their
nonsense for an up-to-date audience, too much articulateness. They
would do better to talk gibberish, perhaps. Now they must change
their style, and find out what really did make people laugh, if people
20 could be made to; but he, the manager, was over fifty and never
good himself at making jokes, even the old-fashioned kind. What
was this word that everyone was using – 'sophisticated'? The audiences were too sophisticated, even the children were: they seemed
to have seen and heard all this before, even when they were too
25 young to have seen and heard it.

'What shall we do?' he asked his wife. They were standing under
the Big Top, which had just been put up, and wondering how many
of the empty seats would still be empty when they gave their first
performance. 'We shall have to do something, or it's a bad look-
30 out.'

'I don't see what we can do about the comic side,' she said. 'It
may come right by itself. Fashions change, all sorts of old things
have returned to favour, like old-time dances. But there's something
we could do.'

35 'What's that?'

'Put on an act that's dangerous, really dangerous. Audiences are
never bored by that. I know you don't like it, and no more do I, but
when we had the Wall of Death –'

Her husband's big chest-muscles twitched under his thin shirt.

40 'You know what happened then.'

'Yes, but it wasn't our fault, we were in the clear.'

He shook his head.

'Those things upset everyone. I know the public came after it
happened – they came in shoals, they came to see the place where
45 someone had been killed. But our people got the needle and didn't
give a good performance for I don't know how long. If you're
proposing another Wall of Death I wouldn't stand for it – besides,
where will you find a man to do it? – especially with a lion on his
bike, which is the great attraction.'

50   'But other turns are dangerous too, as well as dangerous-looking. It's *being* dangerous that is the draw.'

'Then what do you suggest?'

Before she had time to answer a man came up to them.

'I hope I don't butt in', he said, 'but there's a man outside who
55   wants to speak to you.'

'What about?'

'I think he's looking for a job.'

'Bring him in', said the manager.

The man appeared, led by his escort, who then went away. He
60   was a tall, sandy-haired fellow with tawny leonine eyes and a straggling moustache. It wasn't easy to tell his age – he might have been about thirty-five. He pulled off his old brown corduroy cap and waited.

'I hear you want to take a job with us,' the manager said, while
65   his wife tried to size up the newcomer. 'We're pretty full up, you know. We don't take on strangers as a rule. Have you any references?'

'No, sir.'

'Then I'm afraid we can't help you. But just for form's sake, what
70   can you do?'

As if measuring its height the man cast up his eyes to the point where one of the two poles of the Big Top was embedded in the canvas.

'I can dive sixty feet into a tank eight foot long by four foot wide
75   by four foot deep.'

The manager stared at him.

'Can you now?' he said. 'If so, you're the very man we want. Are you prepared to let us see you do it?'

'Yes,' the man said.
80   'And would you do it with petrol burning on the water?'

'Yes.'

'But have we got a tank?' the manager's wife asked.

'There's the old Mermaid's tank. It's just the thing. Get somebody to fetch it.'

85   While the tank was being brought the stranger looked about him.

'Thinking better of it?' said the manager.

'No, sir,' the man replied. 'I was thinking I should want some bathing-trunks.'

'We can soon fix you up with those,' the manager said. 'I'll show
90   you where to change.'

Leaving the stranger somewhere out of sight, he came back to his wife.

'Do you think we ought to let him do it?' she asked.

'Well, it's his funeral. You wanted us to have a dangerous act,
95   and now we've got it.'

'Yes, I know, but –' The rest was drowned by the rattle of the trolley bringing in the tank – a hollow, double cube like a sarcophagus. Mermaids in low relief sported on its leaden flanks. Grunting and muttering to each other the men slid it into position, a few feet
100   from the pole. Then a length of hosepipe was fastened to a faucet,

butt in (*l.54*): interrupt
tawny (*l.60*): brown
leonine (*l.60*): like a lion
straggling (*l.61*): long and untidy (moustache)
references (*l.66*): letters from previous employers
foot (*l.74*): approx. 31 cms (3 feet = a little less than 1 metre)
sarcophagus (*l.97*): stone coffin (used in ancient times)
faucet (*l.100*): water tap

and soon they heard the sound of water swishing and gurgling in the tank.

'He's a long time changing,' said the manager's wife.

105 'Perhaps he's looking for a place to hide his money,' laughed her husband, and added, 'I think we'll give the petrol a miss.'

At length the man emerged from behind a screen, and slowly walked towards them. How tall he was, lanky and muscular. The hair on his body stuck out as if it had been combed. Hands on hips he stood beside them, his skin pimpled by goose-flesh. A fit of

110 yawning overtook him.

'How do I get up?' he asked.

The manager was surprised, and pointed to the ladder. 'Unless you'd rather climb up, or be hauled up! You'll find a platform just below the top, to give you a foot-hold.'

115 He had started to go up the chromium-plated ladder when the manager's wife called after him: 'Are you still sure you want to do it?'

'Quite sure, madam.'

He was too tall to stand upright on the platform, the awning

120 brushed his head. Crouching and swaying forty feet above them he swung his arms as though to test the air's resistance. Then he pitched forward into space, unseen by the manager's wife who looked the other way until she heard a splash and saw a thin sheet of bright water shooting up.

125 The man was standing breast-high in the tank. He swung himself over the edge and crossed the ring towards them, his body dripping, his wet feet caked with sawdust, his tawny eyes a little bloodshot.

'Bravo!' said the manager, taking his shiny hand. 'It's a first-rate act, that, and will put money in our pockets. What do you want for

130 it, fifteen quid a week?'

The man shook his head. The water trickled from his matted hair on to his shoulders, oozed from his borrowed bathing-suit and made runnels down his sinewy thighs. A fine figure of a man: the women would like him.

135 'Well, twenty then.'

Still the man shook his head.

'Let's make it twenty-five. That's the most we give anyone.'

Except for the slow shaking of his head the man might not have heard. The circus-manager and his wife exchanged a rapid glance.

140 'Look here,' he said. 'Taking into account the draw your act is likely to be, we're going to make you a special offer – thirty pounds a week. All right?'

Had the man understood? He put his finger in his mouth and went on shaking his head slowly, more to himself than at them, and

145 seemingly unconscious of the bargain that was being held out to him. When he still didn't answer, the knot of tension broke, and the manager said, in his ordinary, brisk voice.

'Then I'm afraid we can't do business. But just as a matter of interest, tell us why you turned down our excellent offer.'

150 The man drew a long breath and breaking his long silence said, 'It's the first time I done it and I didn't like it.'

swishing, gurgling (l.101): noises made by water

give . . . a miss (l.105): not do something

lanky (l.107): tall and thin

A fit of yawning (l.109): suddenly began to yawn a lot

be hauled up (l.113): be pulled up with a rope

awning (l.119): roof of the circus tent

pitched (l.122): fell forward suddenly

bloodshot (l.127): red in the eyes

quid (l.130): pounds sterling (slang)

the knot . . . (l.146): everyone relaxed because the final decision had been made

With that he turned on his heel and straddling his long legs walked off unsteadily in the direction of the dressing-room.

The circus-manager and his wife stared at each other.

155 'It was the first time he'd done it,' she muttered. 'The first time.' Not knowing what to say to him, whether to praise, blame, scold or sympathize, they waited for him to come back, but he didn't come.

'I'll go and see if he's all right,' the circus-manager said. But in two minutes he was back again. 'He's not there,' he said. 'He must

160 have slipped out the other way, the crack-brained fellow!'

straddling (l.152): with his
legs wide apart
crack-brained (l.160): crazy

ⓚ Exercise 5

Read the story to find out which of the following statements are *true* and which are *false*. If it is not clear from the story, write *don't know*.

a) The clowns were more successful before 1939 than after.
b) The circus-manager and his wife didn't like jokes.
c) Someone had been killed at the circus.
d) The tall man had worked in a circus before.
e) The man hurt himself when he dived.
f) The manager and his wife really wanted to employ the diver.
g) No one else in that circus was paid £30 per week.
h) The man left because he didn't like the circus-manager.

ⓚ Exercise 6

Find these phrases in the story, and notice the way in which they are used. In each case circle a), b) or c) to show which you think is the best equivalent. Show which examples are correct in the same way. Of these, usually at least two are correct.

1 'Attendances had been falling off' (*line 1*)
  a) nobody was coming to the circus
  b) people who came were not interested
  c) fewer people came to the circus than before

2 'more pointless' (*line 11*)
  a) more a waste of time
  b) not sharp or funny
  c) more amusing

3 Which of these are correct:
  a) She was a pointless doctor.
  b) It's pointless waiting for him.
  c) The programme was pointful.

4 'it just didn't go down' (*line 16*)
  a) no one could understand it
  b) people didn't find it funny
  c) it was too stupid

5 'I wouldn't stand for it' (*line 47*)

    a) I wouldn't permit it
    b) I couldn't bear it
    c) I wouldn't like it

6 'It's *being* dangerous that's the draw' (*line 51*)

    a) dangerous acts are a good idea
    b) dangerous acts make people come
    c) being dangerous is enjoyable

7 'led by his escort' (*line 59*)

    a) leading the other man
    b) following the other man
    c) the other man was holding his arm

8 'size up the newcomer' (*line 65*)

    a) calculate how tall he was
    b) attract his attention
    c) see what sort of person he was

Ⓚ **Exercise 7**

a) Match these verbs of eating and drinking (some taken from the story) with the nouns which fit best, using a dictionary if necessary.

munch	chocolate
chew	an ice cream
suck	an apple
gobble	soup
sip	gum
gulp	cake
swallow	coffee
lick	meat
gnaw	sandwich
	popcorn
	chicken bones
	sweets

b) Look at *lines 131–2*. Now group the verbs related to water (and other liquids) under the headings below.

trickle   gurgle   drip   pour   gush   swish   ooze
flood   flow

Move slowly in small quantities	Move smoothly in quantities	Make a watery noise

c) **Group these words taken from the passage under the headings below. Then try to give an example using each, to help you to remember them.**

stare   grunt   slide   call   sway   praise   mutter
swing   shake   scold   glance   size up

Ways of speaking	Ways of moving	Ways of looking

Exercise 8

Write an alternative ending to the story from just after the moment when the thin man dived off the platform:

'Then he pitched forward into space, unseen by the manager's wife who looked the other way . . .'

Exercise 9

Discuss the following.

a) Why do you think the man in the story agreed to do the dive? How did he feel afterwards?

b) Why do people like to see dangerous acts and stunts? What are they hoping to see?

c) Which of the following do you prefer to watch, and why? Label your three favourites (1, 2 and 3).

- circus acts
- sports matches or events (which ones?)
- plays at the theatre
- dance (e.g. ballet)
- car or motorbike races
- rock concerts or other music festivals
- fireworks
- other (what?) _____

About the Author

Leslie Poles Hartley was born in 1895 in England. After his time at Oxford University, he began writing. He completed eighteen novels, the most famous of which were *The Go-Between* and *The Hireling*. Both were made into films.

The Hireling won the principal prize at the Cannes Film Festival in 1973, the year after Hartley died.

9 Eye Witness

by Ed McBain

Ⓚ Exercise 1

a) Crime is a problem in most countries, especially in the large cities. Here is a list of some criminals and the crimes they commit, but it is incomplete. Fill in the missing parts. Use a dictionary if necessary.

Criminal	Crime	The criminal ...
thief	robbery/theft	stole some jewellery
murderer	_____	killed a policeman
_____	hijacking	hijacked a plane
drug { dealer / pusher	drug { dealing / pushing	_____
_____	kidnapping	kidnapped a rich business man
rapist	_____	raped a young woman
_____	mugging	_____
car thief	_____	stole a Rolls Royce
_____	robbery	_____
terrorist	_____	committed an act of terrorism (e.g. bombing, murder, kidnapping)

b) Which is the worst kind of crime in your opinion? Why? Discuss with a partner.

Ⓚ Exercise 2

Look at these adjectives. Match the opposites by drawing a line between them. Then say which you would use to describe the work of the police in modern cities. Explain why you have chosen them.

dangerous	difficult
pleasant	satisfying
tiring	safe
demanding	unpleasant
frustrating	relaxing
easy	undemanding

Exercise 3

Look at the two photographs. With a partner, invent a story in which the two are connected.

This story is set in an imaginary American city, very similar to New York. It is about a violent crime and the problems the police have solving it. Be ready for a twist at the end.

Eye Witness

He had seen a murder, and the sight had sunken into the brown pits that were his eyes. It had tightened the thin line of his mouth and given him a tic over his left cheekbone.

5   He sat now with his hat in his hands, his fingers nervously exploring the narrow brim. He was a thin man with a moustache that completely dominated the confined planes of his face.

He was dressed neatly, his trousers carefully raised in a crease-protecting lift that revealed taut socks and the brass clasp of one garter.

10   'That him?' I asked.

'That's him,' Magruder said.

'And he saw the mugging?'

'He says he saw it. He won't talk to anyone but the lieutenant.'

'None of us underlings will do, huh?'

15   Magruder shrugged. He'd been on the force for a long time now, and he was used to just about every type of taxpayer. I looked over to where the thin man sat on the bench against the wall.

'Well,' I said, 'let me see what I can get out of him.'

Magruder cocked an eyebrow and asked, 'You think maybe the

20   Old Man *would* like to see him personally?'

Glossary

tic (*l.3*): nervous movement of face muscles

brim (*l.5*): the edge of a hat

dominated (*l.6*): was the most obvious feature

crease-protecting (*l.7*): the man had pulled up his trousers so that his knees would not smooth out the creases

garter (*l.9*): elastic to hold up socks or stockings

shrugged (*l.15*): lifted his shoulders as if to say 'I don't know why.'

on the force (*l.15*): in the police

Old Man (*l.20*): the boss

75

'Maybe. If he's got something. If not, we'd be wasting his time. And especially on this case, I don't think...'

'Yeah,' Magruder agreed.

I left Magruder and walked over to the little man. He looked up when I approached him, and then blinked.

'Mr Struthers?'

'Yes,' he said warily.

'I'm Detective Cappeli. My partner tells me you have some information about the...'

'You're not the lieutenant, are you?'

'No,' I said, 'but I'm working very closely with him on this case.'

'I won't talk to anyone but the lieutenant,' he said. His eyes met mine for an instant, and then turned away. He was not being stubborn, I decided. I hadn't seen stubbornness in his eyes. I'd seen fear.

'Why, Mr Struthers?'

'Why? Why what? Why won't I tell my story to anyone else? Because I won't, that's why.'

'Mr Struthers, withholding evidence is a serious crime. It makes you an accessory after the fact. We'd hate to have to...'

'I'm not withholding anything. Get the lieutenant, and I'll tell you everything I saw. That's all, get the lieutenant.'

I waited for a moment before trying again. 'Are you familiar with the case at all, sir?'

Struthers considered his answer. 'Just what I read in the papers. And what I saw.'

'You know that it was Lieutenant Anderson's wife who was mugged? That the mugger was after her purse and killed her without getting it?'

'Yes, I know that.'

'Can you see then why we don't want to bring the lieutenant into this until it's absolutely necessary? So far, we've had ten people confessing to the crime, and eight people who claim to have seen the mugging and murder.'

'I *did* see it,' Struthers protested.

'I'm not saying you didn't, sir. But I'd like to be sure before I bring the lieutenant in on it.'

'I just don't want any slip-ups,' Struthers said. 'I...I don't want him coming after me next.'

'We'll offer you every possible protection, sir. The lieutenant, as you can well imagine, has a strong personal interest in this case. He'll certainly see that no harm comes to you.'

Struthers looked around him suspiciously. 'Well, do we have to talk here?'

'No, sir, you can come into my office.'

He deliberated for another moment, and then said, 'All right.' He stood up abruptly, his fingers still roaming the hat brim. When we got to my office, I offered him a chair and a cigarette. He took the seat, but declined the smoke.

'Now then, what did you see?'

'I saw the mugger, the man who killed her.' Struthers lowered his

If he's got something (l.21): if he really knows who did it
blinked (l.25): closed his eyes and opened them quickly
warily (l.27): carefully
accessory after the fact (l.40): guilty of helping the criminal after the crime has been committed
purse (l.48): handbag (American English)
deliberated (l.66): thought carefully

voice. 'But he saw me, too. That's why I want to make absolutely certain that . . . that I won't get into any trouble over this.'

'You won't, sir. I can assure you. Where did you see the killing?'

75 'On Third and Elm. Right near the old paint factory. I was on my way home from the movies.'

'What did you see?'

'Well, the woman, Mrs Anderson – I didn't know it was her at the time, of course – was standing on a corner waiting for the bus. I 80 was walking down toward her. I walk that way often, especially coming home from the show. It was a nice night and . . .'

'What happened?'

'Well, it was dark, and I was walking pretty quiet, I guess. I wear gummies – gum sole shoes.'

85 'Go on.'

'The mugger came out of the shadows and grabbed Mrs Anderson around the throat, from behind her. She threw up her arm, and her purse opened and everything inside fell on the sidewalk. Then he lifted his hand and brought it down, and she screamed, and he 90 yelled, "Quiet, you bitch!" He lifted his hand again and brought it down again, all the time yelling, "Here, you bitch, here, here," while he was stabbing her. He must have lifted the knife at least a dozen times.'

'And you saw him? You saw his face?'

95 'Yes. She dropped to the ground, and he came running up the street toward me. I tried to get against the building, but I was too late. We stood face to face, and for a minute I thought he was going to kill me, too. But he gave a kind of a moan and ran up the street.'

'Why didn't you come to the police at once?'

100 'I . . . I guess I was scared. Mister, I still *am*. You've got to promise me I won't get into any trouble. I'm a married man, and I got two kids. I can't afford to . . .'

'Could you pick him out of a line-up? We've already rounded up a lot of men, some with records as muggers. Could you pick the 105 killer?'

'Yes. But not if he can see me. If he sees me, it's all off. I won't go through with it if he can see me.'

'He won't see you, sir. We'll put you behind a screen.'

'So long as he doesn't see me. He knows what I look like, too, 110 and I got a family. I won't identify him if he knows I'm the one doing it.'

'You've got nothing to worry about.' I clicked down Magruder's toggle on the intercom, and when he answered, I said, 'Looks like we've got something here, Mac. Get the boys ready for a run-115 through, will you?'

'Right. I'll buzz you.'

We sat around and waited for Magruder to buzz.

'I won't do it unless I'm behind a screen,' Struthers said.

'You'll have a one-way mirror, sir.'

120 We'd waited for about five minutes when the door opened. A voice lined with anguish and fatigue said, 'Mac tells me you've got a witness.'

gum sole (l.84): shoes with soft bottoms

moan (l.98): sound of pain or unhappiness

line-up (l.103): a line of people including those suspected of a crime (witnesses have to recognise the person they saw)

toggle (l.113): button, knob

intercom (l.113): internal phone

buzz (l.116): call (on the phone)

I turned from the window, ready to say, 'Yes, sir,' and Struthers turned to face the door at the same time.

125   His eyebrows lifted, and his eyes grew wide.

He stared at the figure in the doorway, and I watched both men as their eyes met and locked for an instant.

'No!' Struthers said suddenly. 'I . . . I've changed my mind. I . . . I can't do it. I have to go. I have to go.'

130   He slammed his hat onto his head and ran out quickly, almost before I'd gotten to my feet.

'Now what the hell got into him all of a sudden?' I asked.

Lieutenant Anderson shrugged wearily. 'I don't know,' he said. 'I don't know.'

slammed (l.130): with a very hard and quick movement (put his hat on)

Ⓚ Exercise 4

Complete the following statements about the story.

1 Mr Struthers looked _____.
2 He didn't want to speak to _____.
3 Cappeli talked to him because he wanted to know _____.
4 The detectives didn't want to trouble the lieutenant because the victim of the murder _____.
5 Struthers was frightened because the murderer _____.
6 Mrs Anderson, the victim, was waiting for a bus when _____.
7 The murderer killed her by _____.
8 Struthers ran out of the police station because _____.

Ⓚ Exercise 5

Find these phrases in the story, and notice the way in which they are used. In each case circle a), b) or c) to show which you think is the best equivalent. Show which examples are correct in the same way. Of these, usually at least two are correct.

1 'had sunken into the brown pits' (*line 1*)
   a) had made him very tired
   b) had made his eyes look full of fear
   c) had made his eyes change colour

2 'None of us underlings will do' (*line 14*)
   a) we aren't qualified to deal with him
   b) he feels he is above our level
   c) he doesn't want to talk to a junior policeman

3 Which of these are correct:
   a) The boss gave the job to an underling.
   b) This container will do – as long as it's big enough.
   c) A: Will you do? B: No. I'm tired.

4 'withholding evidence'
  (*line 39*)

   a) keeping information secret
   b) giving wrong information
   c) pretending to have information

5 Which of these are correct:

   a) The police are withholding the man for questioning.
   b) The parents withheld their permission.
   c) His salary was withheld until he had signed the contract.

6 'confessing to the crime' (*line 53*)

   a) arrested for the crime
   b) saying they have evidence
   c) saying they committed the crime

7 'I don't want any slip-ups'
  (*line 58*)

   a) I don't want to fall down
   b) I don't want anyone to be stupid
   c) I don't want any mistakes

8 'suspiciously' (*line 63*)

   a) angrily
   b) as if he didn't trust Capelli
   c) in a frightened way

9 'declined the smoke' (*line 69*)

   a) showed he didn't like the smoke
   b) took the cigarette but didn't light it
   c) refused the cigarette

10 'wearily' (*line 133*)

   a) tiredly
   b) unhappily
   c) angrily

Ⓚ **Exercise 6**   **Many of the following words occur in the story. The ones on the left are related in some way to the ones on the right. Can you make pairs?**

raise	eye
knife	tired
shoulder	eyebrow
fatigue	wander
lower	stab
blink	mutter
roam	shrug
moan	drop

Exercise 7

In *line 45*, Struthers says that he has read about the case in the papers, as well as being an eye-witness. Write a report of the kind you think he read. Begin like this.

BRUTAL MURDER ON THIRD STREET

Yesterday evening around 11 p.m. the body of a woman was found on Third Street at the corner with Elm . . .

Exercise 8

The story is about a crime. Answer these questions.

a) Do you read crime stories or watch films or series on T.V.?

If yes:
Which of the following are most important for you in a good crime story or film or T.V. series?

If no:
Why not? Is it for any of the following reasons?

- suspense
- a lot of action
- characters who you can identify with
- violence and blood

- a happy ending
- realistic atmosphere

- other (what?) _____

- boring
- unrealistic
- characters who you don't recognise
- too many frightening surprises
- too much violence
- reminds you of unpleasant things

- other (what?) _____

b) Which of these characteristics does this story have? Discuss with a partner.

Ⓚ Exercise 9

In the first three lines of the story, McBain gives the reader a good idea of how affected Struthers is by his terrifying experience. List five other words or phrases used in the story to build up this impression of a terrified man. Do you think McBain's way of doing it is successful?

About the Author

Ed McBain (whose real name is Evan Hunter) was born in New York. After serving in the US Navy in the Second World War, he went back to college and began to work as assistant to a literary agent. In this job – deciding which of the stories and books sent to the agent were good ones to try to publish – McBain learnt about story writing. Then his boss started selling McBain's own stories and a novel, so he retired to write full time.

Since then he has written many novels about work in the police department, the famous '87th Precinct' series. These are based on inside knowledge of police stations in New York.

10 You Are Now Entering the Human Heart

by Janet Frame

Exercise 1

Look at the title of the story. What do you think it is going to be about?
- doctors performing an operation
- an imaginary journey through the human body
- a visit to a museum
- a love relationship
- other (what?) _____

Why?

Ⓚ **Exercise 2**

Everybody experiences fear at some time or other, for example when you are woken by a strange noise at night, before you go to the dentist, or when you are on top of a high building. The following words describe different kinds of fear. Using a dictionary if necessary, put the words in the appropriate place on the lines. You may want to put more than one word on a line.

afraid   nervous   terrified   petrified   scared   frightened

A little fear

_____
_____
_____
_____
_____

A lot of fear

Exercise 3

Look at the list of animals and fish below. Are you afraid of any of them? Write the numbers 1 to 4 beside the four which frighten you most (1 = most frightening). Then compare your choices with somebody else. Explain why you are afraid of the animals.
- crocodile
- tarantula
- snake
- vampire bat
- large rat
- shark
- scorpion
- tiger
- piranha
- octopus

Exercise 4
Look at the two photographs. With a partner, invent a story in which they are related.

The author of this story is from New Zealand, but the story is set in Philadelphia, the largest city in Pennsylvania, USA. The narrator is visiting an unusual museum there.

You Are Now Entering the Human Heart

I looked at the notice. I wondered if I had time before my train left Philadelphia for Baltimore in one hour. The heart, ceiling-high, occupied one corner of the large exhibition hall, and from wherever you stood in the hall you could hear its beating, *thum-thump-thum-*
5 *thump.* It was a popular exhibit, and sometimes, when there were too many children about, the entrance had to be roped off, as the children loved to race up and down the blood vessels and match their cries to the heart's beating. I could see that the heart had already been punished for the day – the floor of the blood vessel
10 was worn and dusty, the chamber walls were covered with marks, and the notice 'You Are Now Taking the Path of a Blood Cell Through the Human Heart', hung askew. I wanted to see more of the Franklin Institute and the Natural Science Museum across the street, but a journey through the human heart would be fascinating.
15 Did I have time?

Later. First, I would go across the street to the Hall of North America, among the bear and the bison, and catch up on American flora and fauna.

I made my way to the Hall. More children, sitting in rows on
20 canvas chairs. An elementary class from a city school, under the control of an elderly teacher. A museum attendant holding a basket,

Glossary

Baltimore (*l.2*): a large city in Maryland, USA
roped off (*l.6*): closed by putting a rope or cord across
blood vessel (*l.7*): a vein or artery through which blood flows round the body
chamber (*l.10*): enclosed space, room
askew (*l.12*): crooked
flora and fauna (*l.18*): plant and animal life

and all eyes gazing at the basket.

'Oh,' I said. 'Is this a private lesson? Is it all right for me to be here?'

25 The attendant was brisk. 'Surely. We're having a lesson in snake-handling,' he said. 'It's something new. Get the children young and teach them that every snake they meet is not to be killed. People seem to think that every snake has to be knocked on the head. So we're getting them young and teaching them.'

30 'May I watch?' I said.

'Surely. This is a common grass snake. No harm, no harm at all. Teach the children to learn the feel of them, to lose their fear.'

He turned to the teacher. 'Now, Miss – Mrs – ' he said.

'Miss Aitcheson.'

35 He lowered his voice. 'The best way to get through to the children is to start with teacher,' he said to Miss Aitcheson. 'If they see you're not afraid, then they won't be.'

She must be near retiring age, I thought. A city woman. Never handled a snake in her life. Her face was pale. She just managed to

40 drag the fear from her eyes to some place in their depths, where it lurked like a dark stain. Surely the attendant and the children noticed?

'It's harmless,' the attendant said. He'd been working with snakes for years.

45 Miss Aitcheson, I thought again. A city woman born and bred. All snakes were creatures to kill, to be protected from, alike the rattler, the copperhead, king snake, grass snake – venom and victims. Were there not places in the South where you couldn't go into the streets for fear of the rattlesnakes?

50 Her eyes faced the lighted exit. I saw her fear. The exit light blinked, hooded. The children, none of whom had ever touched a live snake, were sitting hushed, waiting for the drama to begin; one or two looked afraid as the attendant withdrew a green snake about three feet long from the basket and with a swift movement, before

55 the teacher could protest, draped it around her neck and stepped back, admiring and satisfied.

'There,' he said to the class. 'Your teacher has a snake around her neck and she's not afraid.'

Miss Aitcheson stood rigid; she seemed to be holding her breath.

60 'Teacher's not afraid, are you?' the attendant persisted. He leaned forward, pronouncing judgement on her, while she suddenly jerked her head and lifted her hands in panic to get rid of the snake. Then, seeing the children watching her, she whispered. 'No, I'm not afraid. Of course not.' She looked around her.

65 'Of course not,' she repeated sharply.

I could see her defeat and helplessness. The attendant seemed unaware, as if his perception had grown a reptilian covering. What did she care for the campaign for the preservation and welfare of copperheads and rattlers and common grass snakes? What did she

70 care about someday walking through the woods or the desert and deciding between killing a snake and setting it free, as if there would be time to decide, when her journey to and from school in down-

brisk (*l.25*): quick and efficient
lurked (*l.41*): waited, trying not be noticed
rattler (*rattlesnake*), *copperhead, king snake, grass snake* (*l.47*): different kinds of American snake
venom (*l.47*): poison (of snakes)
withdrew (*present; withdraw*) (*l.53*): took out (formal English)
draped (*l.55*): arranged (like a scarf)

town Philadelphia held enough danger to occupy her? In two years or so, she'd retire and be in that apartment by herself and no doorman, and everyone knew what happened then, and how she'd be afraid to answer the door and to walk after dark and carry her pocketbook in the street. There was enough to think about without learning to handle and love the snakes, harmless and otherwise, by having them draped around her neck for everyone, including the children – most of all the children – to witness the outbreak of her fear.

'See, Miss Aitcheson's touching the snake. She's not afraid of it at all.'

As everyone watched, she touched the snake. Her fingers recoiled. She touched it again.

'See, she's not afraid. Miss Aitcheson can stand there with a beautiful snake around her neck and touch it and stroke it and not be afraid.'

The faces of the children were full of admiration for the teacher's bravery, and yet there was a cruelly persistent tension; they were waiting, waiting.

'We have to learn to love snakes,' the attendant said. 'Would someone like to come out and stroke teacher's snake?'

Silence.

One shamefaced boy came forward. He stood petrified in front of the teacher.

'Touch it,' the attendant urged. 'It's a friendly snake. Teacher's wearing it around her neck and she's not afraid.'

The boy darted his hand forward, rested it lightly on the snake, and immediately withdrew his hand. Then he ran back to his seat. The children shrieked with glee.

'He's afraid,' someone said. 'He's afraid of the snake.'

The attendant soothed. 'We have to get used to them, you know. Grownups are not afraid of them, but we can understand that when you're small you might be afraid, and that's why we want you to learn to love them. Isn't that right, Miss Aitcheson? Isn't that right? Now who else is going to be brave enough to touch teacher's snake?'

Two girls came out. They stood hand in hand side by side and stared at the snake and then at Miss Aitcheson.

I wondered when the torture would end. The two little girls did not touch the snake, but they smiled at it and spoke to it and Miss Aitcheson smiled at them and whispered how brave they were.

'Just a minute,' the attendant said. 'There's really no need to be brave. It's not a question of bravery. The snake is *harmless*, absolutely *harmless*. Where's the bravery when the snake is harmless?'

Suddenly the snake moved around to face Miss Aitcheson and thrust its flat head toward her cheek. She gave a scream, flung up her hands, and tore the snake from her throat and threw it on the floor, and, rushing across the room, she collapsed into a small canvas chair beside the Bear Cabinet and started to cry.

I didn't feel I should watch any longer. Some of the children began to laugh, some to cry. The attendant picked up the snake and

pocketbook (*l.77*): handbag (American English)
shrieked with glee (*l.101*): screamed with excitement
soothed (*l.103*): spoke in a gentle way

nursed it. Miss Aitcheson, recovering, sat helplessly exposed by the
125 small piece of useless torture. It was not her fault she was city-bred,
her eyes tried to tell us. She looked at the children, trying in some
way to force their admiration and respect; they were shut against
her. She was evicted from them and from herself and even from her
own fear-infested tomorrow, because she could not promise to love
130 and preserve what she feared. She had nowhere, at that moment,
but the small canvas chair by the Bear Cabinet of the Natural
Science Museum.

I looked at my watch. If I hurried, I would catch the train from
Thirtieth Street. There would be no time to make the journey
135 through the human heart. I hurried out of the museum. It was
freezing cold. The icebreakers would be at work on the Delaware
and the Susquehanna: the mist would have risen by the time I arrived
home. Yes, I would just catch the train from Thirtieth Street. The
journey through the human heart would have to wait until some
140 other time.

evicted (l.128): rejected
icebreakers (l.136): ships used
to break through thick ice
*Delaware, Susquehanna
(l.136):* rivers in the
Eastern USA

Ⓚ Exercise 5

Answer the following questions about the story.
1 Why did the narrator go to the museum?
2 What kind of person was the attendant she spoke to?
3 Why did he put the snake round the teacher's neck?
4 Why did the teacher fall over and cry?
5 Was the snake a dangerous one?
6 How did the narrator feel about what happened?

Ⓚ Exercise 6

**Find these phrases in the story, and notice the way in which they are
used. In each case circle a), b) or c) to show which you think is the
best equivalent. Show which examples are correct in the same way.
Of these, usually at least two are correct.**

1 'ceiling-high' (*line 2*)
   a) as high as the ceiling
   b) hung at the height of the ceiling
   c) on the ceiling

2 'catch up on' (*line 17*)
   a) pretend I was hunting
   b) see them in a short time
   c) learn more about

3 'no harm' (*line 31*)
   a) it doesn't matter if you watch
   b) the snake won't hurt you
   c) the snake isn't dangerous

4 Which of these are correct:
   a) Don't harm him.
   b) Tobacco is harmful.
   c) It makes harm to the environment.

5 'hushed' (*line 52*)
    a) excited
    b) quietly
    c) whispering

6 'recoiled' (*line 84*)
    a) moved away instinctively
    b) closed round the snake
    c) felt stiff

7 'stroke it' (*line 87*)
    a) squeeze it
    b) touch it gently, as if it was a cat
    c) hold it in your hands

8 Which of these are correct:
    a) He stroked the dog.
    b) The stone he threw stroked me on the head.
    c) She stroked his arm.

9 'Grownups' (*line 104*)
    a) mature children
    b) big boys
    c) adults

10 'collapsed' (*line 120*)
    a) fell
    b) crashed
    c) sat

Ⓚ Exercise 7

The words below are all taken from the story.

hushed (*l. 52*)   satisfied (*l. 56*)   urged (*l. 97*)
jerked (*l. 62*)   collapsed (*l. 120*)   panic (*l. 62*)
admiration (*l. 89*)   glee (*l. 101*)   scream (*l. 118*)
sharply (*l. 65*)   soothed (*l. 103*)   leaned forward (*l. 61*)
rigid (*l. 59*)   whispered (*l. 63*)   defeat (*l. 66*)
darted (*l. 99*)

a) Group them in the table below according to whether they are used to describe the behaviour of Miss Aitcheson, the attendant or the children.

Miss Aitcheson	The Attendant	The Children
_____ _____	_____ _____	_____ _____
_____ _____	_____ _____	_____ _____
_____ _____	_____ _____	_____ _____

b) Now indicate whether the words relate to the speech (S), movement (M) or feelings (F) of the three people by writing the correct letter (S, M or F) beside each word.

Exercise 8

Discuss the following questions in pairs.

a) How do the characters in the story develop and change as the story progresses?

b) Imagine this had happened to one of your teachers when you were a young child. What would you have felt?

You may want to use one or more of these words:

sorry for	unsympathetic
embarrassed	amused
upset	shocked etc.

c) Have you ever seen anyone get as terrified as Miss Aitcheson did (in real life or in a film)? Why was it? What did they do?

Exercise 9

Imagine you are Miss Aitcheson, and that you keep a diary. Write the diary entry for that day. Begin like this:

'Today was one of the worst days of my life. I've never felt so humiliated. I took my class to the Natural Science Museum for a talk about snakes (not my favourite animals). Suddenly the attendant . . .

Ⓚ Exercise 10

The writer builds up the tension in Miss Aitcheson until we are prepared for some sort of drama, e.g. *lines 39–40* 'Her face was *pale*. She just managed to *drag the fear from her eyes*'. Find at least six other phrases which you think describe her feelings well.

About the Author

Janet Frame was born in New Zealand in 1924. She has written at least ten novels, including *Living in Maniotot*, which won a New Zealand Book Award, and four collections of short stories. In addition, she has written a book for children and an autobiography, the first part of which also won a prize.

11 Old Man at the Bridge

by Ernest Hemingway

Exercise 1 Which animal(s) would you like to have as a pet? Write the numbers 1 to 3 beside your favourites. Give reasons. Put ✗ beside those you definitely would *not* like to have as pets. Give reasons.

- cat
- large dog
- snake
- hamster
- pigeons or doves
- other birds (which?) _____

- goat
- small dog
- rabbit
- turtle or tortoise
- fish (which?) _____
- other animals (which?) _____

Exercise 2 All war is horrible both for the military personnel involved and for the civilians in the war zones. Imagine some of the things that have happened to people during the wars since 1936. Use the words below (look up the ones you don't know in a dictionary).

Nouns	Verbs
plane, helicopter	fly (flew), crash (-ed) into
bomb	bomb (-ed), drop (-ped)
gun, machine gun	shoot (shot), fire (-d), wound (-ed)
missile	fire, hit (hit)
destruction	destroy (-ed), damage (-d), burn (burnt)
belongings	lose (lost)
evacuation	evacuate (-d)
fresh food	grow (grew)
prisoner; refugee	arrest (-ed), imprison (-ed)
	kill (-ed), die (-d)

Exercise 3 Look at the two photographs at the top of the next page. With a partner invent a story in which the two are related.

88

This story takes place during the Spanish Civil War. This war was between the Republicans (a group of political parties on the left including the socialists, the communists and the anarchists, who wanted rapid change in Spain) on one side, and right wing conservatives (including the Falange and the army, who wanted to maintain the traditional order) on the other. This is the side Hemingway calls the Fascists. They were led by General Franco and helped by Hitler and Mussolini. Many people from Britain, the USA and other countries volunteered to fight for the other side, the Republicans. The war began in 1936 and finally ended in 1939 with victory for the Fascists. General Franco was president of Spain until he died in 1975.

Old Man at the Bridge

An old man with steel rimmed spectacles and very dusty clothes sat by the side of the road. There was a pontoon bridge across the river and carts, trucks, and men, women and children were crossing it. The mule-drawn carts staggered up the steep bank from the bridge
5 with soldiers helping push against the spokes of the wheels. The trucks ground up and away heading out of it all; the peasants plodded along in the ankle-deep dust. But the old man sat there without moving. He was too tired to go any farther.

It was my business to cross the bridge, explore the bridgehead
10 beyond and find out to what point the enemy had advanced. I did this and returned over the bridge. There were not so many carts now and very few people on foot, but the old man was still there.

'Where do you come from?' I asked him.

'From San Carlos,' he said, and smiled.

15 That was his native town and so it gave him pleasure to mention it and he smiled.

'I was taking care of animals,' he explained.

'Oh,' I said, not quite understanding.

Glossary

pontoon bridge (*l.2*): bridge made of floating metal sections (usually constructed by soldiers)
spokes of the wheels (*l.5*): the bars connecting the centre of the wheels and the outer edge
ground up and away (*l.6*): went up slowly and noisily
peasants (*l.6*): country people who work on the land
ankle-deep (*l.7*): the dust was covering their feet
bridgehead (*l.9*): a defensive area on the side of a bridge which is nearer the enemy

'Yes,' he said, 'I stayed, you see, taking care of animals. I was the
20 last one to leave the town of San Carlos.'

He did not look like a shepherd nor a herdsman and I looked at
his black dusty clothes and his grey dusty face and his steel rimmed
spectacles and said, 'What animals were they?'

'Various animals,' he said, and shook his head. 'I had to leave
25 them.'

I was watching the bridge and the African-looking country of the
Ebro Delta and wondering how long now it would be before we
would see the enemy, and listening all the while for the first noises
that would signal that ever mysterious event called contact, and the
30 old man still sat there.

'What animals were they?' I asked.

'There were three animals altogether,' he explained. 'There were
two goats and a cat and then there were four pairs of pigeons.'

'And you had to leave them?' I asked.

35 'Yes. Because of the artillery. The captain told me to go because
of the artillery.'

'And you have no family?' I asked, watching the far end of the
bridge where a few last carts were hurrying down the slope of the
bank.

40 'No,' he said, 'only the animals I stated. The cat, of course, will
be all right. A cat can look out for itself, but I cannot think what
will become of the others.'

'What politics have you?' I asked.

'I am without politics,' he said. 'I am seventy-six years old. I have
45 come twelve kilometres now and I think now I can go no farther.'

'This is not a good place to stop,' I said. 'If you can make it, there
are trucks up the road where it forks for Tortosa.'

'I will wait a while,' he said, 'and then I will go. Where do the
trucks go?'

50 'Towards Barcelona,' I told him.

'I know of no one in that direction,' he said, 'but thank you very
much. Thank you again very much.'

He looked at me very blankly and tiredly, then said, having to
share his worry with someone, 'The cat will be all right, I am sure.
55 There is no need to be unquiet about the cat. But the others. Now
what do you think about the others?'

'Why, they'll probably come through it all right.'

'You think so?'

'Why not?' I said, watching the far bank where now there were no
60 carts.

'But what will they do under the artillery when I was told to leave
because of the artillery?'

'Did you leave the dove cage unlocked?' I asked.

'Yes.'

65 'Then they'll fly.'

'Yes, certainly they'll fly. But the others. It's better not to think
about the others,' he said.

'If you are rested I would go,' I urged. 'Get up and try to walk
now.'

shepherd, herdsman (l.21): a
person who looks after
sheep, goats, cattle etc.
that would signal . . . contact
(l.29): that would show
that the fighting (between
Facists and Republicans)
had begun again
artillery (l.35): heavy guns
which can fire long
distances
'What politics have you?'
(l.43): 'Which side in the
war do you support?'
dove cage (l.63): place where
the pigeons were kept

70 'Thank you,' he said and got to his feet, swayed from side to side and then sat down backwards in the dust.

'I was only taking care of animals,' he said dully, but no longer to me. 'I was only taking care of animals.'

There was nothing to do about him. It was Easter Sunday and the 75 Fascists were advancing toward the Ebro. It was a grey overcast day with a low ceiling so their planes were not up. That and the fact that cats know how to look after themselves was all the good luck that old man would ever have.

swayed (*l.70*): moved from side to side (as if about to fall)

ⓚ Exercise 4

According to the story, which of the following complete the sentence best.

1 The old man was sitting near the bridge because
   a) he was waiting for someone
   b) he was too tired to go on
   c) the soldiers had told him to stay there
2 The narrator had orders to
   a) discover where the enemy army was
   b) make sure that everybody crossed the bridge and left the area
   c) guard the bridge
3 The old man left San Carlos because
   a) he was ordered to leave
   b) he was frightened
   c) the town was being bombed by the enemy
4 The old man was most worried about
   a) his pigeons
   b) his cat
   c) his goats
5 The narrator
   a) took the old man with him
   b) told the old man to go to Barcelona
   c) left the old man at the bridge because he couldn't do anything about him

ⓚ Exercise 5

On the map at the top of the next page, write the numbers 1, 2 and 3 to indicate where the following were.

1 the Fascist army
2 trucks that were taking people towards Barcelona
3 the old man

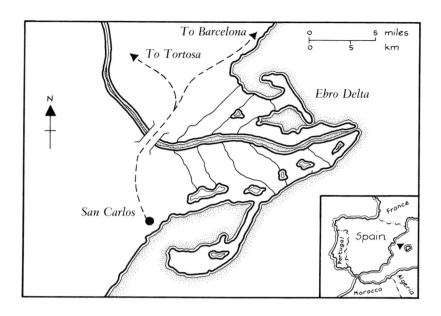

(K) Exercise 6

Find these words and phrases in the story, and notice the way in which they are used. In each case circle a), b) or c) to show which you think is the best equivalent. Show which examples are correct in the same way. Of these, usually at least two are correct.

1 'steel-rimmed spectales'
   (*line 1*)
   a) guns made of steel
   b) glasses with steel frames
   c) suitcases made partly of steel

2 'mule-drawn' (*line 4*)
   a) pulled by animals like horses
   b) as if in an artist's picture
   c) badly designed

3 Which of these are correct:
   a) They travelled in a horse-drawn bus.
   b) This was drawn by a great artist.
   c) The carriage was engine-drawn.

4 'steep' (*line 4*)
   a) high above the level of the river
   b) rising in a sharp gradient, difficult to climb
   c) dangerously exposed

5 Which of these are correct:
   a) The building is very steep.
   b) They climbed a steep hill.
   c) Prices have risen steeply since 1986.

92

6 'plodded along' (*line 7*)
  a) ran quickly
  b) moved anxiously
  c) walked slowly and tiredly

7 'his native town' (*line 15*)
  a) the town where he lived
  b) the town he knew best
  c) the town where he was born

8 Which of these are correct:
  a) I am a native of London.
  b) She is a native-speaker of English.
  c) Is this your native house?

9 'slope of the bank' (*line 38*)
  a) the steep side of the bank
  b) the bottom of the bank
  c) the middle of the bank

10 Which of these are correct:
  a) The house was built on a slope.
  b) The garden slopes down to the river.
  c) The pens rolled off the sloping table.

11 'dully' (*line 72*)
  a) in a bored way
  b) in a sad way
  c) in a tired and sad way

12 'overcast' (*line 75*)
  a) cloudy
  b) unhappy
  c) windy

Ⓚ **Exercise 7** **The verbs below (some taken from the story) can all be used to describe the way people move on foot. Group them in the table below.**

stagger   hurry   rush   jog   plod   stride   race

Walk		Run	
slow	**fast**	**slow**	**fast**

Exercise 8

Do you agree or disagree with the following? What are your reasons? Give examples to support them. Complete the questionnaire. Then discuss your answers with two partners.

- Ordinary people suffer more than the military in wartime.
- No country should ever start a war with another country.
- Every country needs strong military forces, but only for defence.
- Civil wars and revolutions happen because people get impatient.
- If there was a war, I would be willing to fight for my country.
- If everybody refused to fight there would be no wars.

Exercise 9

Imagine you are a British or American newspaper reporter who was in the area at the time, and crossed the bridge with the refugees. Write a report for your newspaper describing the effects of war on ordinary people (you may want to mention the old man, whom you photographed). Begin like this.

FASCISTS CLOSE IN ON EBRO DELTA

Republican forces today retreated towards the Ebro as the Fascists closed in. Again, hundreds of civilians were on the move, leaving their homes and their possessions behind in the hope of escaping the artillery bombardments...

ⓚ Exercise 10

In the story, Hemingway uses quite a lot of repetition: for example, in *line 22*, he uses 'dusty' twice, and the narrator repeats the same question in *lines 23* and *31*. Find more examples of repetition. In each case, say what you think the reason for the repetition is and whether you think it is effective.

About the Author

Ernest Hemingway was born in Chicago in 1899. One of his first jobs was as a newspaper reporter in the First World War. In the 1920s he settled in Paris and began writing. His first famous novels were *Fiesta, Men without Women* and *A Farewell to Arms*, which deals with life in the First World War. Hemingway visited Spain during the Civil War, and described his experiences in the novel *For Whom the Bell Tolls*. In 1954 he was awarded the Nobel Prize for Literature after the publication of *The Old Man and the Sea*. Hemingway shot himself in 1961.

12 Embroidery

by Ray Bradbury

Exercise 1   **Which of these 'science fiction' situations is more likely to come true one day? Put a tick (✔) beside any you think may one day happen. Then compare your list with someone else's.**
- man will explore other galaxies light-years away
- the earth will be visited or invaded by beings from outer space
- human life will be attacked by some strange new animal or plant life
- human life will be (nearly) destroyed by a change in temperature
- the earth will be badly damaged by a meteorite storm
- human life will be (nearly) destroyed by nuclear explosions or other human actions/accidents (e.g. chemical explosions, biological accidents, robots)
- it will become possible to freeze human beings so that they can wake up hundreds of years from now
- other (what?) _____

Exercise 2   **Try to imagine a very frightening and dangerous situation in which there is a very good chance of death (e.g. avalanche; crash; terrorists; fire; being bitten by a poisonous snake; war etc.).**
If you were suddenly in this situation, which of the following would you do? Indicate with a tick (✔).
- scream
- put my arms round a friend
- faint
- pray
- continue to do whatever I was doing at the time
- something different (what?) _____
- keep calm
- close my eyes
- lie down with my arms over my head

Ⓚ **Exercise 3**   **Look at the following words. Using a dictionary if necessary, put them in the correct column below. Where possible, find nouns related to the words, and add other related words if you wish.**

flash   catch fire   silver   light up   bright   explosive
explode   brilliant

Verbs	Nouns	Adjectives
to flash(ed)	a flash	

Now describe an explosion you have seen in a film, on T.V. or in real life. Use words from these lists (and other words you know) to describe it to someone.

Exercise 4

Look at the two pictures. With a partner invent a story in which they could be related.

This story is set in the near future, in a country area of the USA. Although it is in the future, the old women in the story are doing something very traditional; embroidery. They are using coloured thread to sew decorative pictures on small pieces of cloth (like the one in the picture). But they seem to be doing it in order to distract themselves from something...

Embroidery

The dark porch air in the late afternoon was full of needle flashes, like a movement of gathered silver insects in the light. The three women's mouths twitched over their work. Their bodies lay back and then imperceptibly forwards, so that the rocking chairs tilted
5 and murmured. Each woman looked to her own hands, as if quite suddenly she had found her heart beating there.

'What time is it?'

'Ten minutes to five.'

'Got to get up in a minute and shell those peas for dinner.'
10 'But –' said one of them.

'Oh yes, I forgot. How foolish of me...' The first woman paused, put down her embroidery and needle, and looked through the open porch door, through the warm interior of the quiet house, to the

96

silent kitchen. There upon the table, seeming more like symbols of

15   domesticity than anything she had ever seen in her life, lay the
mound of fresh-washed peas in their neat, resilient jackets, waiting
for her fingers to bring them into the world.

    'Go hull them if it'll make you feel good,' said the second woman.

    'No,' said the first. 'I won't. I just won't.'

20   The third woman sighed. She embroidered a rose, a leaf, a daisy
on a green field. The embroidery needle rose and vanished.

    The second woman was working on the finest, most delicate piece
of embroidery of them all, deftly poking, finding, and returning the
quick needle upon innumerable journeys. Her quick black glance

25   was on each motion. A flower, a man, a road, a sun, a house; the
scene grew under her hand, a miniature beauty, perfect in every
threaded detail.

    'It seems at times like this that it's always your hands you turn to,'
she said, and the others nodded enough to make the rockers rock

30   again.

    'I believe,' said the first lady, 'that our souls are in our hands. For
we do *everything* to the world with our hands. Sometimes I think we
don't use our hands half enough; it's certain we don't use our
heads.'

35   They all peered more intently at what their hands were doing.
'Yes,' said the third lady, 'when you look back on a whole lifetime,
it seems you don't remember faces so much as hands and what they
did.'

    They recounted to themselves the lids they had lifted, the doors

40   they had opened and shut, the flowers they had picked, the dinners
they had made, all with slow or quick fingers, as was their manner
or custom. Looking back, you saw a flurry of hands, like a ma-
gician's dream, doors popping wide, taps turned, brooms wielded,
children spanked. The flutter of pink hands was the only sound; the

45   rest was a dream without voices.

    'No supper to fix tonight or tomorrow night or the next night after
that,' said the third lady.

    'No windows to open or shut.'

    'No coal to shovel in the basement furnace next winter.'

50   'No papers to clip cooking articles out of.'

    And suddenly they were crying. The tears rolled softly down their
faces and fell into the material upon which their fingers twitched.

    'This won't help things,' said the first lady at last, putting the back
of her thumb to each under-eyelid. She looked at her thumb and it

55   was wet.

    'Now look what I've done!' cried the second lady, exasperated.
The others stopped and peered over. The second lady held out her
embroidery. There was the scene, perfect except that while the
embroidered yellow sun shone down upon the embroidered green

60   field, and the embroidered brown road curved towards an embroidered pink house, the man standing on the road had something
wrong with his face.

    'I'll just have to rip out the whole pattern, practically, to fix it
right,' said the second lady.

resilient (*l.16*): elastic, able to
  take their shape again

deftly (*l.23*): with great skill

flurry (*l.42*): sudden quick
  movement

wielded (*l.43*): controlled
  with the hands

spanked (*l.44*): smacked on
  the behind

flutter (*l.44*): noise like a
  small birds' wings

furnace (*l.49*): boiler for
  heating the house

rip (*l.63*): to tear roughly

65 'What a shame.' They all stared intently at the beautiful scene with the flaw in it.

The second lady began to pick away at the thread with her little deft scissors flashing. The pattern came out thread by thread. She pulled and yanked, almost viciously. The man's face was gone. She
70 continued to seize at the threads.

'What are you *doing*?' asked the other woman.

They leaned and saw what she had done.

The man was gone from the road. She had taken him out entirely.

They said nothing but returned to their own tasks.
75 'What time is it?' asked someone.

'Five minutes to five.'

'Is it supposed to happen at five o'clock?'

'Yes.'

'And they're not sure what it'll do to anything, really, when it
80 happens?'

'No, not sure.'

'Why didn't we stop them before it got this far and this big?'

'It's twice as big as ever before. No, ten times, maybe a thousand.'
85 'This isn't like the first one or the dozen later ones. This is different. Nobody knows what it might do when it comes.'

They waited on the porch in the smell of roses and cut grass.

'What time is it now?'

'One minute to five.'
90 The needles flashed silver fire. They swam like a tiny school of metal fish in the darkening summer air.

Far away a mosquito sound. Then something like a tremor of drums. The three women cocked their heads, listening.

'We won't hear anything, will we?'
95 'They say not.'

'Perhaps we're foolish. Perhaps we'll go right on, after five o'clock, shelling peas, opening doors, stirring soups, washing dishes, making lunches, peeling oranges . . .'

'My, how we'll laugh to think we were frightened by an old
100 experiment!' They smiled a moment at each other.

'It's five o'clock.'

At these words, hushed, they all busied themselves. Their fingers darted. Their faces were turned down to the motions they made. They made frantic patterns. They made lilacs and grass and trees
105 and houses and rivers in the embroidered cloth. They said nothing, but you could hear their breath in the silent porch air.

Thirty seconds passed.

The second woman sighed finally and began to relax.

'I think I just *will* go shell those peas for supper,' she said. 'I –'
110 But she hadn't time even to lift her head. Somewhere, at the side of her vision, she saw the world brighten and catch fire. She kept her head down, for she knew what it was. She didn't look up, nor did the others, and in the last instant their fingers were flying; they didn't glance about to see what was happening to the country, the
115 town, this house, or even this porch. They were only staring down

flaw (l.66): defect in quality
yanked (l.69) seize at (l.70): pulled roughly
cocked (l.93): tipped to one side
hushed (l.102): silent

at the design in their flickering hands.

The second woman watched an embroidered flower go. She tried to embroider it back in, but it went, and then the road vanished, and the blades of grass. She watched a fire, in slow motion, almost,
120 catch upon the embroidered house and unshingle it, and pull each threaded leaf from the small green tree in the hoop, and she saw the sun itself pulled apart in the design. Then the fire caught upon the moving point of the needle while still it flashed; she watched the fire come along her fingers and arms and body, untwisting the yarn of
125 her being so painstakingly that she could see it in all its devilish beauty, yanking out the pattern from the material at hand. What it was doing to the other women or the furniture or the elm tree in the yard, she never knew. For now, yes now! it was plucking at the white embroidery of her flesh, the pink thread of her cheeks, and at
130 last it found her heart, a soft red rose sewn with fire, and it burned the fresh, embroidered petals away, one by delicate one . . .

unshingle (*l.120*): take the roof covering off
hoop (*l.121*): the round wooden frame holding the embroidery tight
yarn (*l.124*): sewing thread
painstakingly (*l.125*): carefully
plucking (*l.128*): pulling sharply, picking

Ⓚ **Exercise 5**

Answer the following questions about the story.
a) Where were the women?
b) The women were unsure about preparing the peas for cooking. Why?
c) Did they decide to prepare the peas after all?
d) Why did they work so busily?
e) In what way was the experiment they knew about different from earlier ones?
f) What happened to the women at five o'clock?

Ⓚ **Exercise 6**

Find these words and phrases in the story, and notice the way in which they are used. In each case circle a), b) or c) to show which you think is the best equivalent. Show which examples are correct in the same way. Of these, usually at least two are correct.

1 'twitched' (*line 3*)
   a) opened
   b) moved in a nervous way
   c) closed suddenly

2 'rocking chair' (*line 4*)
   a) a chair that tips backwards and forwards
   b) a rock used as a seat
   c) a chair that moves from side to side

3 'murmured' (*line 5*)
   a) made a noise like someone speaking
   b) made a quiet noise
   c) made a loud, unpleasant noise

4 'paused' (*line 11*)

   a) stood up
   b) finished her work, not intending to continue
   c) stopped for a while, intending to continue

5 Which of these are correct:

   a) The workers did a pause for a rest.
   b) She paused, then went on talking.
   c) Use the pause button to stop the tape for a moment.

6 'mound' (*line 16*)

   a) a pile or heap
   b) a kind of container
   c) a measure of weight

7 'sighed' (*line 20*)

   a) made a gesture with her hand
   b) let out a breath in sadness, frustration
   c) put her name on the embroidery

8 'innumerable' (*line 24*)

   a) short
   b) beautiful
   c) very many

9 'miniature' (*line 26*)

   a) very quick
   b) very small
   c) very detailed

10 'souls' (*line 31*)

   a) spirits
   b) hearts
   c) brains

11 'viciously' (*line 69*)

   a) madly
   b) violently
   c) unhappily

12 'they made frantic patterns' (*line 104*)

   a) they sewed in an hysterical way
   b) their embroidery was very beautiful
   c) they moved their hands very carefully

13 'apart' (*line 122*)
    a) to one side
    b) into pieces
    c) towards the middle

14 'devilish' (*line 125*)
    a) incredible
    b) superb, marvellous
    c) bad, evil

Ⓚ Exercise 7

Complete the following in a suitable way by looking at the story again and discussing it with someone else.

a) Hands are important in the story because _____.

b) The women cry because they are thinking about _____.

c) The second woman made a mistake when she was embroidering _____. Because of it she _____.

d) The second woman was just going to prepare the peas when _____.

e) The fire destroyed _____.

Ⓚ Exercise 8

The verbs on the left all describe actions mentioned in the story. Match them with suitable objects on the right.

nod	your hand
lift	the earth
pick	the window
shut	the television
turn on	the coffee
shovel	strawberries
clip out	your head
peel	the advertisement
stir	the potatoes

Exercise 9

Complete the following questionnaire in groups of three.
Do we need more scientific research in these areas (✔ = yes ✘ = no)?

	✔ Why?	✘ Why not?
• Production of energy • Weapons for defence • Weapons for attack • Cures for diseases • Space exploration • Exploration under the sea • Creation of human life • Other — what?		

Exercise 10

Imagine you are one of the women. Two months before these events you write to your senator about the experiments that are being carried out at the testing site a few miles away. Begin the letter like this.

Hooverville
Kansas

Senator W. Smith
The US Senate
Capitol Hill
Washington DC   28 July 1996

Dear Senator Smith,

    We are writing to you to express our worries about the experiments that have been carried out over the last few years at the Johnson Military Testing Site just a few miles from Hooverville...

Ⓚ Exercise 11

In the story, Bradbury uses lists several times. For example, in _line 20_ we find: 'She embroidered a rose, a leaf, a daisy...'. Sometimes the lists are not just words but similar phrases or sentences. Find at least three more examples, and in each case say what the effect of the list is on the development of the story.

Exercise 12

What do you think is the main 'message' of this story, and how do you feel after reading it? What do you like/dislike about it?

About the Author

Ray Bradbury is one of the greatest writers of science and horror fiction of the twentieth century. He was born in Illinois, USA in 1920. As a child he was already fascinated by monsters, dinosaurs and the 'red planet', Mars. He started writing short stories at the age of twelve, and by the 1940s he was making his living out of writing.

    One of his most famous collections is _The Martian Chronicles_, which contains only stories set on Mars. Many of his other stories have been adapted for T.V. and the cinema. For example, _Fahrenheit 451_, which is about a future time when all books are banned and systematically destroyed, was made famous in a film by François Truffaut in 1966.

Key to Exercises

Note: Where answers are given in phrases and sentences, other ways of expressing the idea are usually possible.

1 The First Day of School

Exercise 1
Positive happy, excited, delighted
Negative frightened, angry, sad, upset, worried
Either shy, proud (because it depends on the context)

Exercise 4
a) false   b) true   c) don't know
d) true   e) false   f) don't know

Exercise 5
a) some of his classmates; the jokes; seeing people behaving 'badly'
b) because he wasn't unhappy, he hadn't been harmed by the experience
c) to buy chewing gum
d) that school isn't so bad; that people of your own age can be fun
e) he told him all about his experiences at school; he tried out some of the jokes on him

Exercise 6
1b)   2a)   3c)   4b)   5a)   6a)b)   7b)   8b)c)   9b)   10c)
11a)

Exercise 7

Jim:	on the way to school	angry with Amy; upset; scared
	arriving at the school building	frightened of Mr Barber; of the schoolbuildings
	in class	excited; delighted with the way others behaved
	in the school yard	delighted with the jokes
	just after school	excited about his experiences
	at home in the evening	happy; pleased; proud of his jokes
Amy:	on the way to school	sorry for Jim; unhappy about having to take him to school
	arriving at school	unhappy; depressed by the buildings
	talking to Mr Barber	angry with him; upset
	just after school	amazed at Jim; proud of him; angry with the school
	at home in the evening	happy; moved to see the father and his son so close

2 Tell Us About the Turkey, Jo

Exercise 1
1 stomach   6 nose   11 lips
2 forehead   7 toes   12 chest
3 wrist   8 thumb   13 shoulder
4 ankle   9 neck   14 knee
5 back   10 scalp   15 chin

Exercise 4
1b)   2a)   3c)   4a)   5b)

Exercise 5

Accident	Result
he fell off a baby's chair	he hit his head, which bled badly
he was kicked by a cow	he was winded in the stomach
a ladder fell on him	he was knocked unconscious

Exercise 6

1b) 2a) 3a)b) 4b) 5a) 6a)c) 7a) 8b)c) 9c) 10c)
11a) 12b)

Exercise 7

a) proud – modest   excited – bored   cheerful – depressed
   eager – reluctant
b) unhappy, unsure, unimpressed, dissatisfied, uninterested
   (disinterested means 'objective', not for one side or the other)

Exercise 10

lines 31–34: ... in his eyes... the blood. *lines 42–43*: 'In the stomach,'... his head. *lines 68–69*: The little boy... his shoulders. *lines 87–88*: 'Oo!'... his feet. *lines 95–96*: The little boy... his eyes.

3 Heat

Exercise 1

volcano	ash; lava; smoke and fumes; black clouds; burnt crops and houses
tidal wave	high wind; floods; falling buildings; cars turned over
earthquake	falling buildings; cars turned over; cracks in the earth; digging for people
hurricane	high wind; falling buildings; cars turned over
landslide/avalanche	falling buildings; digging for people
forest/bush fire	high wind; flames; ash; smoke and fumes; black clouds; burnt crops and houses

Exercise 4

a) true   b) false   c) don't know   d) false
e) true   f) false   g) don't know   h) true

Exercise 5

1b) 2a)c) 3a) 4b)c) 5b) 6a) 7b)c) 8a) 9b) 10c)
11b)c)

Exercise 6

Happened in Martinique: Happened in Dominica:
2, 3, 5, 8, 11   1, 4, 6, 7, 9, 10, 12

Exercise 7

stagger into a hospital feeling ill
frighten a child with ghost stories
survive a fall off a three-storey building
seize the money from the till and run away
boil some milk in a saucepan
refuse to wait for her any longer
flicker like a candle in the wind
flood all the streets of a town near the river
twist someone's arm until they say 'Ouch'
stare at someone's strange clothes
gossip about the neighbours
tie a rope round his waist before climbing up
shake hands with someone
wonder why someone is late/about the neighbours
escape from a prison cell by digging a tunnel

Exercise 10
Possible examples.
- personal details   *lines 35–37*: My mother . . . to bed.
- gossip/legend   *lines 53–65*: It was . . . wonder.
- later reading   *lines 69–74*: However . . . survived.
- memories   *lines 24–28*: In the afternoon . . . the ash.

a) The story's details are 'disorganised' in this way perhaps because the writer is showing how we recall past events through a confusing mixture of memories.
b) *lines 27–28*: . . . if I'd like . . .
   lines 41–43: That was . . . flooding in.
   lines 53–54: It was . . . well.

Such informal language gives the story a conversational style, like a person chatting. This is effective because memories and gossip (like that in the story) are often mixed up in conversation.

4 A Shadow

Exercise 3

Adjective to describe a film, book etc.	Adjective to describe a person's feelings	Verb	Noun
boring	bored	to bore	boredom
depressing	depressed	to depress	depression
sad	sad	(to sadden)	sadness
fascinating	fascinated	to fascinate	fascination
amusing	amused	to amuse	amusement
———	angry	to anger	anger
horrifying	horrified	to horrify	horror
———	enthusiastic	———	enthusiasm
	relieved	to relieve	relief
	joyful		joy
absorbing	absorbed	to absorb	absorption
unbearable	———	to bear	———
surprising	surprised	to surprise	surprise
exciting	excited	to excite	excitement
delightful	delighted	to delight	delight
interesting	interested	to interest	interest

(add other words of the same kind as you find them)

Exercise 5
a) Because his father had written and acted in it before he died. It was the only way for him to see his father again after his death.
b) It was a modern story about a girl who didn't want to get married at the usual age but wanted to study. It was more like an English film.
c) No, she didn't. She couldn't bear the idea of seeing her husband on the screen in a film, knowing he was dead. But Sambu managed to persuade her/She finally went to please Sambu.
d) She became so emotional that she fainted/She started crying and then she fainted.
e) He felt very sad at the thought of his mother's unhappiness, and because he would not be able to see his father again, even at the cinema, because they were changing the film the following day.

Exercise 6
1c)   2a)c)   3a)   4a)   5c)   6b)   7b)c)   8a)   9b)   10a)
11b)   12b)

Exercise 7
a) B   b) R   c) F   d) R   e) B   f) R   g) F   h) R

Exercise 8
a) ...it was a Tamil film and he didn't like Tamil films (presumably he preferred films in English or Hindi)
b) ...writing the film (script) and acting in it
c) ...hadn't seen his father/had been missing his father, so he felt very enthusiastic about going to the film/so he felt quite sad (lonely)
d) ...not so/as good as/worse than the girls
e) ...she was worried about his school work/lessons
f) ...there were separate seats (sections) for women and men
g) ...she was dead (as well as his father)
h) ...he knew it was the last time he would see the film/his father, and because his mother had been so upset by it

Exercise 9

Related to ways of speaking			Related to ways of feeling	
quiet	normal	angry	good/happy	bad/unhappy
whisper mutter	explain declare	demand sneer quarrel	eagerly hope delighted relief joy	dread bear depressed longed missed

5 I Spy

Exercise 4
a) false   b) true   c) don't know   d) true   e) don't know
f) false   g) false   h) true   i) true

Exercise 5
1c)   2a)   3b)   4a)   5a)   6a)   7a)c)   8c)   9b)c)   10b)
11b)   12a)b)   13c)   14a)   15b)   16a)   17a)c)

Exercise 6
Light probed, shone, pale, reflected, burst, burn, haze, flashed
Sound creaked, note, beating, snore, dry, muttered

Exercise 7
1 A stitch in time saves nine (if you do something at the right time you can save yourself a lot of trouble later)
2 You may as well be hung for a sheep as for a lamb (if you are going to get caught for a crime, it may as well be a big crime)
3 Never put off till tomorrow what you can do today (do things immediately if you can—don't delay)
4 People who live in glasshouses shouldn't throw stones (don't criticise other people if you are in danger of being criticised yourself)
5 While there's life there's hope (don't give up until you're dead)
6 Don't look a gift horse in the mouth (if somebody offers you something free, don't criticise it)
7 Every cloud has a silver lining (even unhappy events may have their good side)

Exercise 10
line 38: ...made him...the hole. *lines 44–47*: For a while...custard,' *lines 56–59*: ...held his breath...caught.' *lines 70–71*: For a moment...thoroughly;

6 Dead Men's Path

Exercise 3

Positive	Negative
energetic	(lazy, lethargic)
(progressive)	unprogressive
(advanced)	backward
(nice, pleasant)	nasty
responsible	(irresponsible)
wonderful	(awful)
enthusiastic	(unenthusiastic, reluctant)
fantastic	(credible, probable)
delightful	(horrible)
admirable	(shameful)

Exercise 5
1 No, he thought he would have to wait much longer.
2 She was particularly interested in changing the look of the school, especially the compound.
3 He thought the school grounds were private and didn't like outsiders coming in.
4 The path was blocked with a fence made of thick pieces of wood and barbed wire.
5 He came because he was worried about the path being closed to the villagers, for whom it was very important.
6 They tore up the hedges and trampled the flowers.

Exercise 6
2 She liked the thought of herself as an important and admired person.
3 He looked rather weak and older than his years, but he was only 26. He was quite handsome.
4 a) Improvement of the school grounds and gardens.
  b) Improvement in teaching standards.
  c) Closure of the path through the school grounds.
5 The path connected the place of worship (the shrine) with the place where people were buried.
6 Mr Obi thought the villagers were backward and should be taught that their superstitions were foolish.
  The village priest thought that people should be allowed to keep their traditional beliefs, and that it was not necessary to change people's attitudes and habits.
7 A woman who was expecting a baby died and the villagers thought that this was because their ancestors were offended by the fence. They destroyed it to avoid more deaths.
8 The inspector was shocked by the state of the school and the conflict between the village and the school, caused by Mr Obi's misguided attitude.

Exercise 7
1b) 2a)b) 3c) 4a) 5a) 6c) 7a) 8c) 9b) 10c)
11a)

Exercise 10
lines 5–6: Obi . . . ideas. *lines 9–11*: He was . . . ones. *line 30*: They . . . school.
lines 91–93: Mr Obi . . . as that. *lines 103–104*: We can . . . burdensome.

7 A Tree Falls

Exercise 2

d) 1 twig
   2 leaves
   3 branches (or boughs)
   4 roots
   5 trunk
   6 sapling
   7 underbrush (or undergrowth)

Exercise 4

a) false   b) true   c) don't know   d) true
e) false   f) false   g) don't know   h) false

Exercise 5

1b)   2a)b)   3c)   4a)   5c)   6b)   7b)c)   8a)   9c)   10b)
11a)   12a)b)   13a)   14b)   15c)   16b)

Exercise 6

a) **Sound** snapping, creak, ringing, echo, grunt, roar, groaned, thundered, crackle
   Movement vibrating, leaped, bowed, kick, reared, somersault, flowed
b) Church bells... ring   Pigs... grunt
   A heavy door... creaks   An acrobat... somersaults/leaps
   A bad telephone line... crackles   A lion... roars
   Actors... bow   A jazz musician's fingers... snap
   An unhappy person... groans   A horse... leaps

Exercise 7

a) • he talks about 'ripples' and 'surface'; the silence is like a pool.
   • *lines 1–3*: ...the waves...flowed back. *lines 54–56*: the ripples... poker-player.
   • comparing silence to smooth water helps the reader to imagine very clearly the smoothness and completeness of the silence.
b) • yes, in *line 119–120*: Was that...at last.; 'giant' can just mean 'very large' but he also talks about the 'great heart of wood'...
   • the writer uses this image to describe the story of the 'battle' between the man and the tree; it makes it more dramatic, like a real physical fight between two people.
c) The message of the story is the smallness and vulnerability of man against the natural world, even when the man is strong and experienced.

8 A High Dive

Exercise 4

a) dangerous – safe   amusing– sad
   tiring   – relaxing   exciting – boring

Exercise 5

a) true   b) false   c) true   d) don't know
e) false   f) true   g) don't know h) false

Exercise 6

1c)   2b)   3b)   4b)   5a)   6b)   7b)   8c)

Exercise 7

a) The verbs of eating and drinking which fit the nouns best are as follows, but
there are also other possibilities.

munch	an apple, popcorn, chocolate, cake etc.
chew	gum, meat
suck	sweets
gobble	most things (= to eat very fast)
sip	coffee, soup (= to take a small drink)
gulp	coffee, soup (= to take a large, fast drink)
swallow	most things
lick	an ice cream
gnaw	chicken bones

b)

Move slowly in small quantities	Move smoothly in large quantities	Make a watery noise
trickle	pour	gurgle
drip	gush	gush
ooze	flood	
	flow	

c)

Ways of speaking	Ways of moving	Ways of looking
mutter	swing	stare
scold	shake	glance
grunt	slide	size up
call	sway	
praise		

9 Eye Witness

Exercise 1

Criminal	Crime	The criminal . . .
thief	robbery/theft	stole some jewellery
murderer	murder	killed a policeman
hijacker	hijacking	hijacked a plane
drug {dealer / pusher}	drug {dealing / pushing}	dealt in / pushed } cocaine
kidnapper	kidnapping	kidnapped a rich business man
rapist	rape	raped a young woman
mugger	mugging	mugged an old lady
car thief	theft	stole a Rolls Royce
robber	robbery	robbed a bank
terrorist	terrorism	committed an act of terrorism (eg. bombing, murder, kidnapping)

Exercise 2

dangerous – safe   pleasant – unpleasant   tiring – relaxing
demanding – undemanding   frustrating – satisfying
easy – difficult

Exercise 4

1 . . . neat but very nervous.
2 . . . to anyone but the lieutenant.
3 . . . whether Struthers had anything important to say.
4 . . . had been his own wife.
5 . . . had seen Struthers' face.
6 . . . she was attacked by the mugger.
7 . . . stabbing her with a knife.
8 . . . he recognised the lieutenant as the mugger.

Exercise 5

1b)   2c)   3a)b)   4a)   5b)c)   6c)   7b)   8c)   9c)   10a)

Exercise 6

raise – eyebrow   knife – stab
shoulder – shrug   fatigue – tired
lower – drop   blink – eye
roam – wander   moan – mutter

Exercise 9

lines 34–35: I hadn't seen stubbornness . . . I'd seen fear.
line 67: . . . his fingers still roaming the hat brim.
line 100: 'I was scared . . . I still am.'
line 125: . . . his eyes grew wide.
line 130: . . . slammed his hat . . . quickly.

10 You Are Now Entering the Human Heart

Exercise 2

A little fear

        nervous
        scared; afraid; frightened
        terrified; petrified

A lot of fear

Exercise 5

1 To pass the time before her train left.
2 A brisk, enthusiastic but rather insensitive man.
3 He wanted to show the children that their teacher wasn't frightened of snakes.
4 Because the snake suddenly moved its head towards her face.
5 No, it was a grass snake.
6 She felt sorry for the teacher and rather angry with the attendant.

Exercise 6

1a)   2c)   3b)   4a)b)   5b)   6a)   7b)   8a)c)   9c)   10a)

Exercise 7

Miss Aitcheson		The Attendant		The Children	
scream	S	soothed	S	hushed	S
protest	S	urged	S	stroke	M
whispered	S	leaned forward	M	darted	M
collapsed	M	satisfied	F	admiration	F
rigid	M			glee	F
jerked	M				
defeat	F				
panic	F				
sharply	F				

Exercise 10

line 50: I saw her fear.
line 59: . . . stood rigid, . . . breath.
line 66: I could see . . . helplessness.
lines 84–85: Her fingers recoiled.
lines 118–121: She gave a scream . . . to cry.
line 124: . . . helplessly exposed . . .

11 Old Man at the Bridge

Exercise 4
1b)   2a)   3a)   4c)   5c)

Exercise 5

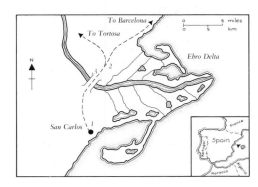

Exercise 6
1b)   2a)   3a)b)   4b)   5b)c)   6c)   7c)   8a)b)   9a)
10a)b)c)   11c)   12a)

Exercise 7

	Walk		Run	
slow	**fast**	**slow**	**fast**
plod stagger	stride hurry	jog	race rush

Exercise 10
lines 17/19: taking care of the animals—old people tend to repeat themselves.
lines 23/31: What animals were they?—the old man doesn't understand the question clearly.
lines 35–36/61–62: because of the artillery—the old man seems fascinated by the word, as if unsure what it means; he's obviously distressed at having to leave home for it.
lines 72–73: I was only taking care of the animals—it's as if the old man is talking to himself in his unhappiness and incomprehension.

12 Embroidery

Exercise 3

Verbs	Nouns	Adjectives
to flash(ed) to catch fire	a flash a fire silver	flashing fiery silver; silvery
to light up to brighten to explode	a light brightness explosion brilliance	light bright explosive brilliant

Exercise 5
a) They were sitting on the porch, outside the house.
b) Because they thought they would probably not get to eat dinner.
c) Yes, but they didn't have time to do it.
d) They were trying to take their minds off the experiment.
e) It was much bigger.
f) They died in the huge explosion.

Exercise 6

1b) 2a) 3b) 4c) 5b)c) 6a) 7b) 8c) 9b) 10a)
11b) 12a) 13b) 14c)

Exercise 7

a) ... they are symbols of life itself (line 31)/in the story the women's hands are always active and they show their feelings in the way they sew

b) ... about their pasts and the emptiness of the future

c) ... the man's face. (Because of it) she picked out the threads/took the man out of the embroidery

d) ... the explosion happened/there was a bright flash in the distance

e) ... first the embroidery, then the women themselves/then travelled along their fingers and arms, through their bodies until it reached their hearts

Exercise 8

nod your head	shovel the earth
lift your hand/head	clip out the advertisement
pick strawberries	peel the potatoes
shut the window	stir the coffee
turn on the television	

Exercise 11

line 25: all these normal, everyday things appear gradually on the embroidered picture; they contrast with the 'experiment' and the suddenness of the final explosion.

lines 39–41: episodes from their lives are being remembered as the end of their lives draws near.

lines 43–44: as above; memories came rushing in, like a flashback in a film.

lines 46–50: suddenly they realise the finality of what is happening. They speak like the chorus in a Greek tragedy, who foresee the disaster at the end of a play.